D0999714

STARS
MOSQUITOES
AND CROCODILES

STARS

MOSQUITOES

The American Travels of

ALEXANDER VON HUMBOLDT

Illustrations by RUSSELL FRANCIS PETERSON

HARPER & ROW, PUBLISHERS,

AND

CROCODILES

Selected and Edited by

MILLICENT E. SELSAM

NEW YORK AND EVANSTON

F 2216
H 91

36271

STARS, MOSQUITOES AND CROCODILES

Copyright © 1962 by Millicent E. Selsam

Printed in the United States of America

All rights reserved.

No part of the book may be used or repro-
duced in any manner whatsoever without
written permission except in the case of
brief quotations embodied in critical articles
and reviews. For information address
Harper & Row, Publishers, Incorporated,
49 East 33rd Street, New York 16, N. Y.

Library of Congress catalog card number: 61-12085

To Robert and Howard

CONTENTS

EDITOR'S NOTE

MANY OF THE WORLD'S GREATEST travel books are neglected because they are long-winded and printed in fine type that is hard to read. Humboldt's *Personal Narrative of Travels to the Equinoctial Regions of America During the Years 1799-1804* is no exception. This masterpiece, describing his experiences in South America, was a best-seller in the early part of the nineteenth century. Yet it has not been reprinted in English for more than a hundred years.

The *Narrative* itself runs to 1,500 pages of fine print and takes the reader only to 1801. This volume contains carefully edited and abridged selections from it, supplemented with excerpts from other writings of Humboldt that describe the remainder of his travels in South America, Cuba, Mexico, and the United States up to 1804.

Readers will be able to follow Humboldt's incredible explorations along the Orinoco River and share his adventures with crocodiles, jaguars, electric eels, and cannibal Indians, and his exciting climb of Mount Chimborazo (20,577 feet)—the highest mountain man had ever climbed up to that time. They will share his amazing scientific investigations, which make his *Narrative* not only a great travel book but also a landmark in the scientific study of the earth. They will come to understand why Humboldt's name appears on maps all over the earth and even on its satellite, the moon.

The selections are from the 1852 English translation of the original French *Narrative*. Supplementary selections are taken from Humboldt's *Views of Nature, Researches Concerning the Institutions and Monuments of the Ancient Inhabitants of America, Political Essay on the Kingdom of New Spain,* and his letters to his brother and friends. (See the list of sources at the end of the book.)

The Introduction tells of Humboldt's position in the history of science and describes his life up to the time of his departure for South America. An epilogue at the end of the book describes Humboldt's later life in Paris and Berlin, where he became the most famous man in Europe with the exception of Napoleon Bonaparte.

The editor has provided bridge passages and notes which supply background material and unify the selections. Technical terms in the text and references to persons and places are explained in brackets. The titles and subtitles of the chapters are the editor's. Cuts within the selections, except for small interpolations and asides, are indicated by dots.

Both science and the world have changed since Humboldt's volumes were written a century and a half ago. But as long as there are jungles and perils from wild animals, as long as there are new plants to find and star-studded heavens to observe, as long as there are new frontiers of knowledge, the travel writings of Alexander von Humboldt will be read and enjoyed.

Millicent E. Selsam
New York, New York, 1962

INTRODUCTION

WHEN A young German set out in a sailing vessel for South America in 1799, few people had ever heard of Baron Alexander von Humboldt.

For five years he and a botanist friend, Aimé Bonpland, wandered in jungles and deserts, boated up and down wild tropical rivers, and climbed snow-covered mountains. Through all their travels they carried the most delicate scientific instruments, which they used to measure mountains, make astronomical and magnetic observations, and to find the exact latitude and longitude and record the temperatures of the places they visited. They also carried equipment to help them make collections of the thousands of animals and plants they found in South America. Humboldt was, Charles Darwin believed, "the most scientific traveler that ever lived."

From all this, mankind reaped a rich harvest. The incredible amount of information Humboldt took back with him to Europe filtered into all branches of science. For Humboldt was explorer, naturalist, astronomer, botanist, geographer, geologist, geophysicist, meteorologist, oceanographer, physiologist, and authority on agriculture, industry, and mining, all rolled into one.

Every geography textbook or atlas owes something to Humboldt. He was the first to draw maps of Mexico and Cuba based on accurate astronomical observations. His maps of South America were studied by the nineteenth-century mapmakers of Europe and became the basis for reliable maps of

Alexander von Humboldt

this area of the world. He was the first to trace lines on maps connecting places that have the same average temperature. Thus "isothermal lines" were introduced into map-making.

Botanists pored over the 60,000 specimens of plants he and Bonpland brought back from the New World. Among them were 3,500 new species. But Humboldt did more than just add new species to the list of those known. He created a field of botanical science which did not exist until his time—the science of plant geography. He was the first to see that there was a relation between climate and the way plants were distributed around the world. He noticed, too, how vegetation changed as one climbed a high mountain, and he compared it to the way vegetation changes as one goes north or south from the equator to the poles.

His contributions to the field of geology were great. He was the first to draw geologic sections to show the rock structure of the earth. He showed the direction of chains of mountains and their geologic structure. He added enormously to our knowledge of volcanoes.

In astronomy he observed the great meteor showers of 1799 and was one of the first to show that such showers occur at regular intervals.

In oceanography he observed the physical properties of ocean waters. He plotted the current in the Pacific later named after him and added considerably to our knowledge of the Gulf Stream and other ocean currents.

He did pioneer experiments in nerve physiology.

He studied magnetic phenomena of the earth. On this subject he became practically an "International Geophysical Year" by himself when he persuaded scientists and governments to take part in a Magnetic Union during the late 1830's.

At fifty stations in different parts of the world, arrangements were made to observe and record magnetic changes simultaneously. In this way, scientists, working together, were able to advance man's knowledge of the forces that make compass needles behave peculiarly.

Humboldt's observations of the Indians of South America and Mexico laid the foundation for much later research in anthropology. He studied the Indians of the Amazon and Orinoco valleys. He examined the monuments of the Incas, Aztecs, and Mayans. His reports of the civilizations they revealed created among Europeans a new level of respect for the natives of the New World. Europe was accustomed to think of them mainly as savages and slaves.

Humboldt was a warm, freedom-loving person with a passionate hatred of slavery. His writings on the history and treatment of Negro slaves, especially in Cuba, became powerful propaganda in the fight to eliminate slavery from the world.

He suggested nine different routes where a canal could be built from the Atlantic to the Pacific and agitated for such a canal for forty years. He himself favored the route where, while Humboldt was still alive, a young American acquaintance built a railroad from Colón to Panama City. In the following century the United States built the Panama Canal over this same route.

Ralph Waldo Emerson called Humboldt one of the wonders of the world who "appear from time to time, as if to show us the possibilities of the human mind, the force and the range of the faculties—a universal man."

But great men are products of the times in which they live. Humboldt's life covered an exciting and turbulent period of European and American history. Born in September, 1769, he was six years old when the American Declaration of Independence was proclaimed. When he was nineteen the Bastille fell, ushering in the French Revolution. He lived through the Napoleonic Wars, which involved nearly all of Europe, and he knew personally and corresponded with Simón Bolívar, the great revolutionary leader of Latin America. During his life there was as yet no unified Germany or Italy, and although he was born and died a Prussian he had also become a citizen of Mexico and spent much of his life in Paris. Through all these years of war and revolution, Humboldt, known to everyone as a staunch believer in republican principles, devoted himself to natural science. Unfortunately, many trips of exploration he planned were prevented by war and political intrigue.

Humboldt's life also spanned a revolution of a different kind—the "Industrial Revolution," which not only increased production through steam power and new machinery but also ushered in a fabulous age of scientific discovery and development. He was connected, directly or indirectly, with an extraordinary number of the men who were making scientific history. A new science of electricity was advancing by leaps and bounds. Humboldt as a very young man carried further the experiments of Galvani on the influence of electricity upon animal nerves and muscles. He had installed on his boyhood home one of the lightning rods Benjamin Franklin invented.

Geology was moving from the pioneer scientific studies and speculations of Professor Abraham Gottlieb Werner, Humboldt's own teacher, to the modern scientific geology of Charles Lyell, whom Humboldt came to know in later years.

Biology developed during Humboldt's lifetime from a static

idea of species created once and for all to the scientific evolutionary theory of Charles Darwin. Humboldt himself loomed large in Darwin's career. As a college student Darwin read Humboldt's travel narratives, and they inspired him to visit the tropics. Humboldt's study of the geographical distribution of plants later helped Darwin formulate his evolutionary theories.

Captain James Cook, on three great voyages around the world between 1769 and 1778, had begun a new era in scientific navigation and exploration. One of Humboldt's most influential early friendships was with George Forster, who had assisted his father as naturalist on Cook's second voyage. Humboldt hoped to do for the vast interiors of continents something of what Cook had done for oceans and shorelines.

A list of some of Humboldt's scientific acquaintances places him in the main stream of nearly a century of science. In addition to those already mentioned, there appear in the correspondence of Humboldt and the records of his life the names of Ampère (electricity), Arago (astronomy), Blumenbach (anatomy and anthropology), Gauss (mathematics), Gay-Lussac (physics), Liebig (organic chemistry), Samuel Morse (telegraphy), Benjamin Silliman of Yale (mineralogy), and Louis Agassiz (biology).

Alexander von Humboldt was born in Berlin in 1769. His father was a major who had fought in the wars of Frederick the Great and who maintained connections with the Prussian court. His mother was of French descent; her Huguenot ancestors had come to Prussia seeking refuge from religious persecution. Alexander's father died when he was ten and his older brother, Wilhelm, was twelve.

The two boys were educated by private tutors. Their winters were spent in Berlin, their summers at their country home in Tegel, a few miles outside the city. The building was an old turreted castle that had been a hunting seat for Frederick the Great. It was primitive and antiquated but beautifully situated beside a pine forest on the shore of a lovely lake. Alexander loved the grounds and woods, but nevertheless found the place a "castle of boredom." "I passed most of that unhappy time [his youth] here at Tegel," he wrote in later years, "among people who loved me and showed me kindness, but with whom I had not the least sympathy, where I was subjected to a thousand restraints. . . ."

Alexander and his brother were tutored in French, Latin, and Greek. Botany, chemistry, and the other sciences were not in the program of their tutors, and Alexander had to study these subjects later, on his own initiative. "Until I reached the age of sixteen," he wrote, "I showed little inclination for scientific pursuits. I was of a restless disposition and wished to be a soldier! This choice was displeasing to my family, who were desirous that I should devote myself to the study of finance, so that I had no opportunity of attending a course of botany or chemistry. . . ."

In 1789 Alexander joined his older brother at the University of Göttingen. For the first time he had teachers in the natural and physical sciences, and they were among the best in all Germany. He attended courses in archaeology, physics, agriculture, languages, the history of trade and commerce, botany, and geology.

Alexander stayed at Göttingen for only one year, then left with George Forster, who had been visiting relatives at Göttingen, on a journey to Holland, London, and Paris. The two of them, walking most of the way, chipped at rocks with geological hammers, studied plants, art, and manufacturing, visited churches, docks, and mines. Forster had achieved fame with his book describing his voyage with Captain Cook. This gave the travelers ready access to great men everywhere they went.

After this trip Alexander enrolled in the Hamburg School of Commerce to study economics and business administration. He did this mostly to please his mother, who hoped her younger son would make a career in business and finance. But business and finance did not really interest Alexander. At Hamburg he attended few regular lectures, but studied languages, history, mathematics, physics, and other natural sciences by himself. He wrote to a friend about the various libraries of professors to which he was allowed access and said, "You will be compelled to admit . . . that it is no less practicable to study at Hamburg than at Göttingen."

After a year at Hamburg, Alexander applied for a job in the Prussian Ministry of Industry and Mines. He saw in mining an opportunity to increase his working knowledge of geology, in which he had become deeply interested. He had already published an essay on his observations of the rocks of the Rhine made during his journey with Forster. The Ministry informed him that if he would get training at the Mining Academy at Freiberg he would receive an appointment.

The young Alexander, now twenty-two years old, proceeded to Freiberg. He had thought he was working hard during his year at Göttingen, and harder still at Hamburg. But now he really worked. From six in the morning till noon the students were underground, studying rocks, minerals, and mining procedures. The afternoons were devoted to classes and the evenings to study.

The following year, 1792, Humboldt completed his studies

and was appointed an Inspector of Mines in the region of Bayreuth. Here he not only brought about greatly increased production of gold and iron but also sought to improve conditions for the miners. Despite the long hours he spent in the mines and in his work on behalf of the miners, he found time to write articles on botany and other subjects for scholarly magazines, and he also published a scientific work, in Latin, on plant physiology. It dealt with the basic life processes of plants that lived underground in mines without light. This work helped to gain him the acquaintance of Wolfgang von Goethe, the great German writer, who shared Humboldt's interest in plants and other branches of natural science. The already famous Goethe had met the two Humboldt boys on a visit to Tegel when they were ten and twelve years old. Now Goethe found Alexander a gifted young man, and their friendship lasted the rest of Goethe's life.

Alexander went on to study more about plants, soils, and rocks. He began experiments on the excitability of nerves and muscles. Then, just as he was appointed a Counselor of Mines at a salary four times his starting one, he wrote an old friend, "My former plans remain undisturbed. I shall resign my post in two years and go to Russia, Siberia, and I don't know where." This was in 1794. Thirty-five years later he did travel across Russia and Siberia on a scientific journey—but he went to many other places first.

In 1795 he was offered a still higher post in mining. He not only declined this honor but informed the Ministry that he intended "to withdraw from any official position with the state." He wanted no official position. In fact, he wanted no position at all. His mining studies and experience were only a steppingstone, only preparation for a scientific expedition, one "for increasing our knowledge of geology and physical science."

When their mother died in 1796, Alexander and Wilhelm received a considerable inheritance, which left them free to pursue their special interests. Wilhelm's was comparative language, and he became one of the most important founders of the modern scientific study of languages. For Alexander the die was cast. He would travel and study and write. He made one travel plan after another. Perhaps he would go to Russia and Siberia, or to North Africa and India. It mattered little. There was much to be learned about the earth and its productions anywhere. But right now Europe was ablaze. The Napoleonic Wars made many trips difficult if not impossible.

Alexander went to Paris, where Wilhelm had settled. This, he thought, would be the best place to find out what possibilities there were for voyages of exploration. Paris was the greatest scientific center in the world at the time. Here Humboldt was in his element. He met mathematicians, chemists, botanists, zoologists, and astronomers. His own two-volume work on muscles and nerves had been published in 1797. Based on thousands of experiments he had performed himself, it had gained the respect of many of the French scientists he was meeting now. Humboldt discussed his work with them, gave lectures, carried on further research, and enjoyed the social life of Paris.

But he constantly kept his goal before him. All of this was preparation for a voyage to distant lands.

Finally, the great chance came. The seventy-year-old Captain Bougainville, who had sailed around the world and discovered many islands in the Pacific, invited Humboldt to go on a new voyage around the world. Then the authorities decided to send, not the elderly Bougainville, but a much younger man, Captain Baudin.

The voyage was to be a long one. Humboldt wrote to a friend in Berlin: "Many of my friends showed discontent at my wanting to be exposed to the hazards of a voyage lasting over five years, but my decision was firmly made. I would have despised myself if I had turned down such a chance to be useful." And then, just when everything was ready, the threat of war with England caused the voyage to be postponed indefinitely.

The one positive thing that emerged from these shattered plans was Humboldt's meeting with a Frenchman, a few years his junior, who was to have sailed with the expedition as botanist. He was Aimé Bonpland, a physician who at twenty-five was exceptionally well trained in anatomy and botany. Humboldt and Bonpland became fast friends and determined to travel together somewhere, somehow.

Then came a chance to sail from Marseilles on a Swedish ship bound for Morocco, Algiers, and Egypt. Humboldt and Bonpland hurried to Marseilles from Paris only to find that the ship had been damaged in a storm and could not make the trip. The two men decided to go to Spain for the winter in the hope they could get a vessel from there to Africa.

In Madrid, Humboldt met Baron de Forell, minister from the court of Saxony, who suggested that Humboldt seek permission to visit the Spanish colonies in America. He arranged a meeting with the king of Spain. The king received Humboldt graciously and listened to his plans for a voyage to the New World. Humboldt was granted a passport with extensive permission to travel in Spanish possessions. Along with the passport, he carried instructions to officers of the colonies to admit him everywhere and give him all facilities, to permit him to transport his instruments, to make astronomical observations, and to collect whatever he chose. Humboldt also carried a Prussian passport, which defined his purpose— "traveling for the acquisition of knowledge."

Humboldt was prepared, as no single individual before or since has ever been, to study land and ocean, rocks, soil, climate, stars, and men. He invested a small fortune in the scientific equipment for the journey. He collected more than thirty instruments, the very best obtainable. They included two telescopes and a microscope; sextants, quadrants, and a surveyor's chain and transit; thermometers, barometers, hygrometers, and a rain gauge; compasses, a dipping magnetic needle, and other instruments to measure variations and changes in intensity of the earth's magnetic field; galvanometers and other instruments for measuring electric currents and atmospheric electricity; chemical instruments and reagents for determining the chemical composition of the atmosphere, mineral waters, soil, and rocks; an instrument for comparing degrees of blueness in the color of the sky; and an apparatus to determine precisely the boiling point of water at different heights above sea level. Along with these he took a big collection of tools to repair damage the instruments might suffer from falling off pack animals.

Humboldt and Bonpland were to embark at La Coruña on the sloop *Pizarro*. The German Humboldt, a slender man of twenty-nine, with his robust French friend Bonpland, twenty-five years old, were bound for South America, scientific exploration, and adventure.

CHAPTER ONE

ACROSS THE ATLANTIC

LEAVING EUROPE

THE MOMENT of leaving Europe for the first time is attended with a solemn feeling. We in vain summon to our minds the frequency of communication between the two worlds. We in vain reflect on the great facility with which, from the improved state of navigation, we traverse the Atlantic. . . . The sentiment we feel when we first undertake so distant a voyage is not the less accompanied by a deep emotion, unlike any other impression we have hitherto felt. Separated from the objects of our dearest affections, entering in some sort on a new state of existence, we are forced to fall back on our own thoughts, and we feel within ourselves a dreariness we have never known before. . . .

We spent two days at La Coruña after our instruments were embarked. A thick fog, which covered the horizon, at length indicated the change of weather we so anxiously desired. On the 4th of June, in the evening, the wind turned to northeast, a point which, on the coast of Galicia, is considered very constant during the summer. The *Pizarro* prepared to sail on the 5th, though we had intelligence that only a few hours previously an English squadron had been seen from the watchtower of Sisarga, appearing to stand towards the mouth of the Tagus. Those who saw our ship weigh anchor asserted that we should be captured in three days and that, forced to follow the fate of the vessel, we should be carried to Lisbon. . . .

The *Pizarro* set sail at two in the afternoon. . . . At half past six we passed the Tower of Hercules, which is the lighthouse of La Coruña and where, from a very remote time, a coal fire is in no way proportionate to the noble construction of so vast an edifice, being so feeble that ships cannot perceive it till they are in danger of striking on the shore. Towards the close of day the wind increased and the sea ran high. We directed our course to northwest in order to avoid the English frigates, which we supposed were cruising off these coasts. About nine we spied the light of a fishing hut at Sisarga, which was the last object we beheld in the west of Europe. . . .

On the 8th, at sunset, we descried from the masthead an English convoy sailing along the coast and steering towards southeast. In order to avoid it we altered our course during the night. From this moment no light was permitted in the great cabin, to prevent our being seen at a distance. This precaution, which was at the time prescribed in the regulations of the packet ships of the Spanish navy, was extremely irksome to us during the voyages we made in the course of the five following years. We were constantly obliged to make use of dark-lanterns to examine the temperature of the water or to read the divisions on the limb of the astronomical instruments. In the torrid zone, where twilight lasts but a few minutes, our operations ceased almost at six in the evening. This state of things was so much the more vexatious to me as from the nature of my constitution I never was subject to seasickness and feel an extreme ardor for study during the whole time I am at sea.

The Pizarro *sailed between the Madeira Islands and the coast of Africa. On the morning of June 19, 1799, it approached Tenerife—the largest of the Canary Islands. Humboldt and Bonpland stayed there for six days, during which time they climbed the volcanic peak that dominates the island. In the following letter to his brother Humboldt describes this excursion.*

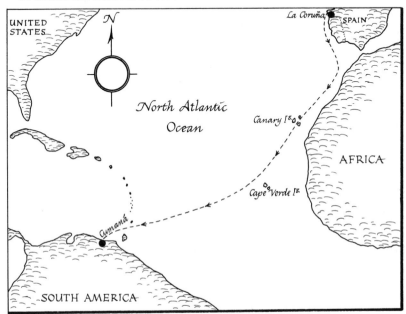

FROM SPAIN TO CUMANÁ

CLIMBING THE VOLCANO OF TENERIFE

I RETURNED last night from an excursion up the Peak. What an amazing scene! What a gratification! We descended some way into the crater, perhaps farther than any previous scientific traveler. No one except Borda and Mason has been even beyond the last cone. There is little danger in the ascent, only fatigue from the trying effects of heat and cold; for the sulphurous vapor in the crater burnt holes in our clothes while our hands were numb in a temperature of 36° [F.].

What a remarkable spectacle was presented to us at this height of 11,500 feet! The dark blue vault of heaven overhead; former streams of lava at our feet; on either side this scene of devastation; three square miles of pumice stone, bordered by groves of laurel, beyond which vineyards interspersed with bananas stretched down to the sea; pretty villages dotted along the coast; the ocean with all the seven islands, among which Palma and Grand Canary are distinguished by lofty volcanoes, spread out before us like a map.

The crater into which we descended emits only sulphurous vapor; the temperature of the ground is 190° [F.]. The lava streams break out at the sides of the mountain, where small craters are formed similar to those by which two years ago the whole island was illuminated. On that occasion a subterraneous noise was heard for two months like the firing of cannon, and stones of the size of a house were hurled into the air to the height of 4,000 feet. I have made some important mineralogical observations here. The Peak is composed of basalt, upon which lie beds of porphyry and obsidian porphyry. Fire and water rage below the surface; I noticed steam escaping from every point. . . .

At the foot of a lava stream in front of the crater we spent the night in the open air . . . at a height of 7,875 feet above the sea. At two in the morning we were already on our way towards the last cone. The heavens were bright with stars, and the moon shone with a gentle radiance; but this calm was soon to be disturbed. The storm raged violently round the summit. We were obliged to cling fast to the edge of the crater. The wind rushed through the rifts with a noise like thunder, while a veil of cloud separated us from the world below. We climbed up the cone as it stood out above the mist, isolated as a ship upon the sea. The sudden change from the beauty of a bright moonlight night to the darkness and desolation of the storm and cloud produced a very impressive effect.

Postscript: In the district of Orotava there is a dragon tree measuring forty-five feet in circumference. Four centuries ago, in the days of the Guanches [the original inhabitants of the Canary Islands], the girth was as great as it is now. I could almost weep at the prospect of leaving this place; I should be quite happy to settle here, and yet I am scarcely out of Europe. Could you but see these luxuriant fields, these forests of laurel, the growth of a thousand years, these vines and these roses! They actually fatten the pigs here upon apricots. The roads are lined with camellias.

We are to sail on the 25th (June).

At Tenerife, Humboldt noticed that the zones of vegetation changed markedly as he climbed the peak. He drew a careful botanical map showing the distribution of plants on this island's 12,000-foot mountain. Near the shore there was a region of vines where all the cultivated plants, olives, fruit trees, grapevines, and wheat were raised. Above this was a region where such trees as oak, laurels, and certain evergreens grew. Above this zone, pines, firs, and junipers were found. These grew up to 6,000 feet, and above this point the ground was covered with broom plant, the flowers of which provided food for the goats. Beyond 11,000 feet the ground was covered with grasses. On the peak itself, nothing grew.

This distribution of plants impressed Humboldt

greatly. Later he saw the same thing on mountains in South America, and his observations led him to lay the foundations of a new science—plant geography.

After leaving Tenerife the **Pizarro** *crossed vast expanses of the Atlantic Ocean and Humboldt kept busy doing experiments with the fine instruments he had taken along. He tested the temperature of the air and the sea, and noted how slowly the temperature of both increased as the ship moved toward the equator. He took readings of the humidity of the air and was astonished at how much*

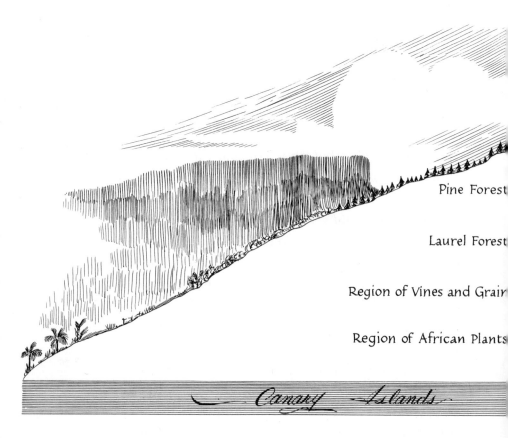

Pine Forest

Laurel Forest

Region of Vines and Grain

Region of African Plants

Canary Islands

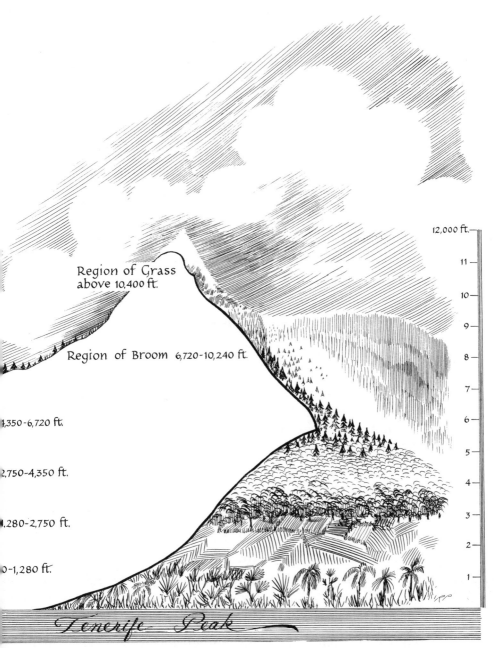

Region of Grass
above 10,400 ft.

Region of Broom 6,720-10,240 ft.

4,350-6,720 ft.

2,750-4,350 ft.

1,280-2,750 ft.

0-1,280 ft.

12,000 ft.
11
10
9
8
7
6
5
4
3
2
1

Tenerife Peak

After a sketch by Humboldt

it increased as they went south. The selection that follows tells of some of Humboldt's astronomical observations on this trip across the Atlantic.

CROSSING THE ATLANTIC

WE LEFT the road of Santa Cruz [Tenerife] on the 25th of June and directed our course towards South America. We soon lost sight of the Canary Islands, the lofty mountains of which were covered with a reddish vapor. The Peak alone appeared from time to time, as at intervals the wind dispersed the clouds that enveloped the Piton. We felt, for the first time, how strong are the impressions left on the mind from the aspect of those countries situated on the limits of the torrid zone, where nature appears at once so rich, so various, and so majestic. Our stay at Tenerife had been very short, and yet we withdrew from the island as if it had long been our home.

Our passage from Santa Cruz to Cumaná [Venezuela], the most eastern part of the New Continent, was very fine. We cut the tropic of Cancer on the 27th; and though the *Pizarro* was not a very fast sailer, we made, in twenty days, the nine hundred leagues [about 3,200 miles] which separate the coast of Africa from that of the New Continent. . . .

From the time we entered the torrid zone, we were never weary of admiring, at night, the beauty of the southern sky, which, as we advanced to the south, opened new constellations to our view. We feel an indescribable sensation when, on approaching the equator and particularly on passing from one hemisphere to the other, we see those stars which we have contemplated from our infancy progressively sink and finally disappear. Nothing awakens in the traveler a livelier remembrance of the immense distance by which he is separated from his country than the aspect of an unknown firmament.

The grouping of the stars of the first magnitude, some scattered nebulae rivaling in splendor the Milky Way, and tracts of space remarkable for their extreme blackness give a peculiar aspect to the southern sky. . . .

The lower regions of the air were loaded with vapors for some days. We saw the Southern Cross distinctly for the first time only on the night of the 4th of July, in the sixteenth degree of latitude. . . . If a traveler may be permitted to speak of his personal emotions, I shall add that on that night I experienced the realization of one of the dreams of my early youth.

The pleasure we felt on discovering the Southern Cross was warmly shared by those of the crew who had visited the colonies. In the solitude of the seas we hail a star as a friend from whom we have long been separated. . . .

THE SOUTHERN CROSS

It has been observed at what hour of the night, in different seasons, the Cross is erect or inclined. It is a timepiece which advances very regularly nearly four minutes a day, and no other group of stars affords to the naked eye an observation of time so easily made. How often have we heard our guides exclaim in the savannas of Venezuela, or in the desert extending from Lima to Truxillo, "Midnight is past, the Cross begins to bend!" . . .

The last days of our passage were not so felicitous as the mildness of the climate and the calmness of the ocean had led us to hope. The dangers of the sea did not disturb us, but the germs of a malignant fever became manifest on board our vessel as we drew near the Antilles. Between decks the ship was excessively hot and very much crowded. From the time we passed the tropic [of Cancer] the thermometer was from 93° to 97° [F.]. Two sailors, several passengers, and, what is remarkable enough, two Negroes from the coast of Guinea and a mulatto child were attacked with a disorder which appeared to be epidemic. The symptoms were not equally alarming in all cases; nevertheless, several persons, and especially the most robust, fell into delirium after the second day. No fumigation was made. A Galician surgeon, ignorant and phlegmatic, ordered bleedings, because he attributed the fever to what he called heat and corruption of the blood. . . .

Those among the passengers who had not yet felt symptoms of the disease resolved to leave the vessel at the first place where she might touch, and await the arrival of another packet, to pursue their course to the island of Cuba and to Mexico. They considered the between decks of the ship as infected; and though it was by no means clear to me that the fever was contagious, I thought it most prudent to land at Cumaná.

The resolution we formed during the night of the 14th of July had a happy influence on the direction of our travels. For, instead of a few weeks, we remained a whole year in this part of the continent. Had not the fever broken out on board the *Pizarro,* we should never have reached the Orinoco, the Casiquiare, or even the limits of the Portuguese possessions on the Río Negro.

CHAPTER TWO

THE NEW WORLD OF THE TROPICS

CUMANÁ

ON THE 16th of July, 1799, at break of day, we beheld a verdant coast of picturesque aspect. The mountains of New Andalusia [now Venezuela], half veiled by mists, bounded the horizon to the south. The city of Cumaná and its castle appeared between groups of coconut palms.

We anchored in the port about nine in the morning, forty-one days after our departure from La Coruña. The sick dragged themselves on deck to enjoy the sight of a land which was to put an end to their sufferings. Our eyes were fixed on the groups of coconut palms which border the river. Their trunks, more than sixty feet high, towered over every object in the landscape. The sun was ascending rapidly toward the zenith. A dazzling light was spread through the air, along the whitish hills strewed with cylindric cactuses, and over a sea ever calm, the shores of which were peopled with pelicans, egrets, and flamingoes. The splendor of the day, the vivid coloring of the vegetable world, the forms of the plants, the varied plumage of the birds—everything was stamped with the grand character of nature in the equatorial regions. . . .

We were conducted by the captain of the *Pizarro* to the governor of the province, Don Vincente Emparán, to present to him the passports furnished to us by the first Secretary of State at Madrid. . . .

The governor of Cumaná expressed his great satisfaction at the resolution we had taken to remain for some time in New Andalusia, a province which at that period was but little known even by name in Europe, and which, in its mountains and on the banks of its numerous rivers, contains a great number of objects worthy of fixing the attention of naturalists. Señor Emparán showed us cottons dyed with native plants, and fine furniture made exclusively of the wood of the country. . . . Señor Emparán was a lover of science, and the public marks of consideration which he gave us during a long abode in his government contributed greatly to procure us a favorable welcome in every part of South America.

The day he arrived in Cumaná, Humboldt wrote to his brother describing his first impressions of the tropics.

FIRST IMPRESSIONS

THE SAME good fortune, my dear brother, which enabled us to run into Tenerife in the face of the English has continued with us to the end of our voyage. I have worked hard all the way, especially with astronomical observations. We intend remaining some months in the [region of] Caracas, where we are truly in a wonderland of fertility and luxuriance; we have on all sides of us extraordinary plants, electric eels, tigers, armadillos, apes, and parrots, besides numbers of genuine Indians—half wild—a very handsome and interesting race.

Cumaná, on account of its proximity to the Snowy Mountains, is one of the coolest and most healthy places in South America, with a climate like that of Mexico; and although it has been visited by Jacquin, the interior of the country is still one of the least-known portions of the globe. Besides the charm of being surrounded by nature in a new aspect (for since yesterday we have not met with a single specimen of a plant or animal common to Europe), we have been mainly influenced in our determination to remain in Cumaná, two days' sail from Caracas, by the news that just now English ships of war are cruising in the neighborhood. It is a voyage of eight or ten days to Havana, and as all European convoys touch here, to say nothing of private merchantmen, we shall not lack opportunities of visiting Cuba. We hear, too, that the heat there is at its worst just in September and October. We shall spend three months, therefore, in the cooler and healthier atmosphere of this place; it is quite possible, even at this temperature, to sleep out at night in the open air.

We have hired a very nice new house . . . and obtained the services of two Negresses, one as a cook. There is no lack of food here, but unfortunately there is nothing to be had in the shape of flour, bread, or biscuit. The town is still half buried in ruins; for the great earthquake of 1797, by which Quito was destroyed, overthrew a considerable part of Cumaná. This town lies in a bay as beautiful as that of Toulon, and is situated at the foot of a range of thickly wooded mountains that rise in the form of an amphitheater to a height of from 5,000 to 8,000 feet. All the houses are built of white cinchona and satinwood. Along the banks of the small river (Río de Cumaná) . . . stand seven monasteries surrounded by plantations which have all the appearance of English gardens. Outside the town live the copper-colored Indians, of whom the men nearly all go naked; their huts are made of bamboo cane covered with the leaves of the coconut palm. On entering one of them, I found the mother and children employing as seats the stems of coral that had been washed up on the shore;

Around Cumaná

they had each a coconut shell before them, to serve the purpose of a plate, from which they were eating fish. The plantations are all open for everyone to go in and out as they please; the inhabitants here are so well disposed that in most of the houses the doors are left open through the night. There are more Indians here than Negroes.

What magnificent vegetation! Coconut palms from fifty to sixty feet in height; Poinciana . . . with pyramidal bunches of flowers a foot high, and of a splendid bright red color; bananas, and a host of trees with enormous leaves and sweet-smelling flowers as large as one's hand, all of which are entirely new. . . . How brilliant the plumage of the birds and the colors of the fishes! Even the crabs are sky-blue and gold!

Hitherto we have been running about like a couple of fools; for the first three days we could settle to nothing, as we were always leaving one object to lay hold of another. Bonpland declares he should lose his senses if this state of ecstasy were to continue. But far more thrilling than the contemplation of these marvelous objects individually is the overpowering sight of the whole mass of such magnificent vegetation, the elegant luxuriance of which is so exhilarating and, at the same time, so soothing. I feel sure I shall be very happy here, and that the agreeable impressions I am now receiving will often cheer me by their inspiring influence.

The first weeks of Humboldt's and Bonpland's stay at Cumaná were employed in testing their instruments, in botanizing in the neighborhood plains, and in examining the traces of the earthquake of December 14, 1797, which had leveled most of the houses of the town.

Humboldt examined the rock structure and was struck with wonder at the similarities of the rocks in the continents of Europe and America. At the time of Humboldt's journey, mineralogists were unacquainted with the name of a single rock of Venezuela, yet Humboldt could identify them because of his knowledge of the rocks of Europe. It was astonishing to him that the earth's crust was so uniform that certain minerals were always grouped together in the layers of rock, and that certain minerals always appeared in the shape of rocky walls or bell-shaped domes just as they did in Europe.

He and Bonpland spent days in the forests collecting plants never before seen by European botanists, and at night classified them as best they could and pressed them between sheets of paper to obtain dried specimens that would last for years. They dried more than 1,600 plants and described about 600 new varieties.

Humboldt also collected shellfish and insects and made his own drawings of the comparative anatomy of these animals.

Numerous visitors came to their house to look at the strange scientific instruments they had brought from Europe. Everybody wanted a chance to look through the telescope at the mountains and craters of the moon. They wanted to see how electricity made a frog's muscles jump, and how the thermometer, barometer, and compass worked. Humboldt and Bonpland answered questions and repeated experiments for hours on end. The one thing that saddened them at Cumaná was the existence of slavery.

SLAVERY IN CUMANÁ

IF THE situation of our house at Cumaná was highly favorable for the observation of the stars and meteorological
phenomena, it obliged us to be sometimes the witnesses of
painful scenes during the day. A part of the great square is
surrounded with arcades, above which is one of those long
wooden galleries common in warm countries. This was the
place where slaves, brought from the coast of Africa, were
sold. Of all the European governments, Denmark was the
first, and for a long time the only, power which abolished the
traffic; yet, notwithstanding that fact, the first Negroes we saw
exposed for sale had been landed from a Danish slave ship.
What are the duties of humanity, national honor, or the laws
of their country to men stimulated by the speculations of
sordid interest?

The slaves exposed to sale were young men from fifteen to
twenty years of age. Every morning coconut oil was distributed
among them, with which they rubbed their bodies to give
their skin a black polish. The persons who came to purchase
examined the teeth of these slaves to judge of their age and
health, forcing open their mouths as we do those of horses in
a market. . . . It is distressing to think that even at this day
there exist European colonists in the West Indies who mark
their slaves with a hot iron, to know them again if they escape.
This is the treatment bestowed on those "who save other men
the labor of sowing, tilling, and reaping."

*Humboldt and Bonpland made two big excursions
from Cumaná. One was to the peninsula of Araya, and the
other to the missions of the Chayma Indians in the mountain areas east of Cumaná.*

On the first trip they examined the salt works at the tip of the Araya peninsula, looked at the ruins of an old castle, and learned of a once thriving pearl fishery off the coast.

The excursion to the mountains led them into the tropical forests.

EXCURSIONS AROUND CUMANÁ

OF ALL the productions on the coasts of Araya, that which the people consider the most extraordinary or, we may say, the most marvelous is "the stone of the eyes." This calcareous [containing calcium carbonate] substance is a frequent subject of conversation, being, according to the natural philosophy of the natives, both a stone and an animal. It is found in the sand, where it is motionless. But if placed on a polished surface—for instance, on a pewter or earthen plate—it moves when excited by lemon juice. If placed in the eye, the supposed animal turns on itself and expels every other foreign substance that has been accidentally introduced.

At the new salt works and at the village of Maniquarez these "stones of the eyes" were offered to us by hundreds, and the natives were anxious to show us the experiment of the lemon juice. They even wished to put sand into our eyes in order that we might ourselves try the efficacy of the remedy.

It was easy to see that the stones are thin and porous opercula (lid-like plates that close the openings of many snails). . . . These calcareous opercula effervesce with lemon juice and put themselves in motion in proportion as the carbonic acid is disengaged. By the effect of a similar reaction, loaves placed in an oven move sometimes on a horizontal plane, a phenomenon that has given occasion in Europe to the popular prejudice of "enchanted ovens."

The "stones of the eyes," introduced into the eye, act like the small pearls and different round grains employed by the American savages to increase the flowing of tears. These explanations were little to the taste of the inhabitants of Araya. Nature has the appearance of greatness to man in proportion as she is veiled in mystery, and the ignorant are prone to put faith in everything that borders on the marvelous. . . .

The inhabitants of Araya, whom we visited a second time on returning from the Orinoco, have not forgotten that their peninsula was one of the points first peopled by the Spaniards. They love to talk of the pearl fishery, of the ruins of the castle of Santiago, which they hope to see someday rebuilt, and of everything that recalls to mind the ancient splendor of those countries. . . .

Our first visit to the peninsula of Araya was soon succeeded by an excursion to the mountains of the missions of the Chayma Indians, where a variety of interesting objects claimed our attention. We entered on a country studded with forests, and visited a convent surrounded by palm trees and tree-like ferns. It was situated in a narrow valley, where we felt the enjoyment of a cool and delicious climate in the center of the torrid zone.

The surrounding mountains contain caverns haunted by thousands of nocturnal birds; and, what affects the imagination more than all the wonders of the physical world, we find beyond these mountains a people lately nomad and still nearly in a state of nature, wild without being barbarous. . . .

When a traveler newly arrived from Europe penetrates for the first time into the forests of South America, he beholds nature under an unexpected aspect. He feels at every step that he is not on the confines, but in the center of the torrid zone, not in one of the West India Islands, but on a vast continent where everything is gigantic—mountains, rivers, and the mass of vegetation. . . . It might be said that the earth, overloaded with plants, does not allow them space enough to unfold themselves. The trunks of the trees are everywhere concealed under a thick carpet of green growth. . . . The same lianas [woody vines] which creep on the ground reach the tops of the trees and pass from one to another at the height of more than a hundred feet. Thus, by the continual interlacing of parasite plants, the botanist is often led to confound one with another, the flowers, the fruits, and leaves which belong to different species.

We walked for some hours under the shade of these arcades, which scarcely admit a glimpse of the sky. . . . In this place we were struck for the first time with the sight of those nests in the shape of bottles, or small bags, which are suspended from the branches of the lowest trees, and which attest the wonderful industry of the orioles, which mingle their warbling with the hoarse cries of the parrots and the macaws. These last, so well known for their vivid colors, fly only in pairs, while the real parrots wander about in flocks of several hundreds. A man must have lived in those regions, particularly in the hot valleys of the Andes, to conceive how these birds sometimes drown with their voices the noise of the torrents which dash down from rock to rock.

One important object of the journey to the missions of the Chayma Indians was a visit to the Cavern of the Guácharo, named for the strange birds that inhabit it. Humboldt was the first scientist to describe these guá-

*charos—night-flying birds that during the day cluster
like bats in the dark caves.*

CAVERN OF THE GUÁCHARO

THAT WHICH confers most celebrity on the valley of Caripe,
besides the extraordinary coolness of its climate, is the great
Cueva, or Cavern, of the Guácharo. In a country where the
people love the marvelous, a cavern which gives birth to a
river and is inhabited by thousands of nocturnal birds, the
fat of which is employed in the missions to dress food, is an
everlasting object of conversation and discussion. . . .

The Cueva del Guácharo is pierced in the vertical profile
of a rock. The entrance is towards the south and forms an arch
eighty feet broad and seventy-two high. The rock which sur-
mounts the grotto is covered with trees of gigantic height . . .
while creeping plants waving in the winds are interwoven in
festoons before the opening of the cavern. . . .

But this luxury of vegetation embellishes not only the external arch; it appears even in the vestibule of the grotto. We
saw with astonishment plantain-leaved heliconias eighteen
feet high, the praga palm tree and tree-like arums following
the course of the river even to those subterranean places. The
vegetation continues in the cave of Caripe as in those deep
crevices of the Andes, half excluded from the light of day, and
does not disappear till, penetrating into the interior, we advance thirty or forty paces from the entrance. We measured
the way by means of a cord and went on about four hundred
and thirty feet without being obliged to light our torches.
Daylight penetrates far into this region because the grotto
forms but one single channel, keeping the same direction from

southeast to northwest. Where the light began to fail we heard from afar the hoarse sounds of the nocturnal birds, sounds which the natives think belong exclusively to those subterranean places. . . .

The plumage of the guácharo is of a dark bluish gray, mixed with small streaks and specks of black. Large white spots of the form of a heart, and bordered with black, mark the head, wings, and tail. The eyes of the bird are blue and are dazzled by the light of day. The spread of the wings, which are composed of seventeen or eighteen quill feathers, is three feet and a half.

The guácharo quits the cavern at nightfall, especially when the moon shines. It is almost the only fruit-eating nocturnal bird yet known. The structure of its feet sufficiently shows that it does not hunt like our owls. . . . It would be difficult to form an idea of the horrible noise occasioned by thousands of these birds in the dark part of the cavern. Their shrill and piercing cries strike upon the vaults of the rocks and are repeated by the subterranean echoes. The Indians showed us the nests of the guácharos by fixing a torch to the end of a long pole. These nests were fifty or sixty feet above our heads, in funnel-shaped holes with which the roof of the grotto is pierced like a sieve. The noise increased as we advanced and the birds were scared by the light of the torches of copal [a resin of tropical trees]. When this noise ceased a few minutes around us, we heard at a distance the plaintive cries of the birds roosting in other ramifications of the cavern. It seemed as if different groups answered each other alternately.

The Indians enter the Cueva del Guácharo once a year, near midsummer. They go armed with poles, with which they destroy the greater part of the nests. At that season several

thousand birds are killed; and the old ones, as if to defend
their brood, hover over the heads of the Indians, uttering
terrible cries. The young, which fall to the ground, are opened
on the spot. The lining of the body cavity is found extremely
loaded with fat, and a layer of fat reaches from the abdomen
to the anus, forming a kind of cushion between the legs of
the bird. This quantity of fat in fruit-eating animals not
exposed to the light and exerting very little muscular motion
reminds us of what has been observed in the fattening of
geese and oxen. It is well known how greatly darkness and
repose favor this process. . . .

At this period, commonly called the oil harvest at Caripe,
the Indians build huts with palm leaves near the entrance and
even in the porch of the cavern. There, with a fire of brushwood, they melt in pots of clay the fat of the young birds just
killed. This fat is known by the name of butter or oil of the
guácharo. It is half liquid, transparent, odorless, and so pure
that it may be kept above a year without becoming rancid.
At the convent of Caripe no other oil is used in the kitchen of
the monks but that of the cavern; and we never observed that
it gave foods a disagreeable taste or smell.

We had great difficulty in persuading the Indians to pass
beyond the front part of the grotto, the only part which they
annually visit to collect the fat. The whole authority of "los
padres" was necessary to induce them to advance as far as
the spot where the soil rises abruptly at an inclination of sixty
degrees, and where the torrent forms a small subterranean
cascade. The natives connect mystic ideas with this cave inhabited by nocturnal birds; they believe that the souls of their
ancestors sojourn in the deep recesses of the cavern. "Man,"

say they, "should avoid places which are enlightened neither by the sun nor by the moon." "To go and join the guácharos" is with them a phrase signifying to rejoin their fathers, to die. . . .

We discharged our guns at random wherever the cries of the nocturnal birds and the flapping of their wings led us to suspect that a great number of nests were crowded together. After several fruitless attempts Monsieur Bonpland succeeded in killing a couple of guácharos which, dazzled by the light of the torches, seemed to pursue us. This circumstance afforded me the means of making a drawing of this bird, which had previously been unknown to naturalists. We climbed, not without difficulty, the small hill whence the subterranean rivulet descends. We saw that the grotto was perceptibly contracted, retaining only forty feet in height, and that it continued stretching to the northeast. . . .

The missionaries, with all their authority, could not prevail on the Indians to penetrate farther into the cavern. As the roof became lower, the cries of the guácharos were more and more shrill. We were obliged to yield to the cowardice of our guides and retrace our steps. . . . Before our eyes became dazzled with the light of day we saw on the outside of the grotto the water of the river sparkling amid the foliage of the trees which shaded it. It was like a picture placed in the distance, the mouth of the cavern serving as a frame. Having at length reached the entrance, we seated ourselves on the bank of the rivulet to rest after our fatigues. We were glad to be beyond the hoarse cries of the birds and to leave a place where darkness does not offer even the charm of silence and tranquillity. We could scarcely persuade ourselves that the name of the Grotto of Caripe had hitherto been unknown in Europe, for

CAVERN OF THE GUÁCHARO

the guácharos alone might have sufficed to render it celebrated.

*Only recently, in 1954, a professor of zoology retraced
Humboldt's footsteps to the Cavern of the Guácharo in
Venezuela. He did not have to climb through a heavy
tropical forest. He was driven in an automobile up to the
entrance of the cave.*

*The scientist was interested in the cries of the guá-
charos described by Humboldt. Did the birds possibly use
these cries to guide themselves in the dark, as bats do?
He found that these birds made high-pitched, click-like
sounds in addition to their screeches. When he plugged
their ears, the birds banged into the walls. He concluded
that these clicks echo back to them and help them navi-*

gate in the dark. Their echo-locating system is like that
of the bats, which use higher-pitched sounds that cannot
be heard by the human ear.

AT THE CAPUCHIN MISSION

THE DAYS we passed at the Capuchin convent in the mountains of Caripe glided swiftly away, though our manner of
living was simple and uniform. From sunrise to nightfall we
traversed the forests and neighboring mountains to collect
plants. When the winter rains prevented us from undertaking
distant excursions, we visited . . . the *conuco* of the community or those assemblies in which the *alcaldes* [officials] every
evening arrange the labors of the succeeding day. We returned
to the monastery only when the sound of the bell called us to
the refectory to share the repast of the missionaries.

Sometimes, very early in the morning, we followed them to
the church to attend the *doctrina*—that is to say, the religious
instruction of the Indians. It was rather a difficult task to explain dogmas to the neophytes [new converts], especially those
who had but a very imperfect knowledge of the Spanish
language. On the other hand, the monks are as yet almost
totally ignorant of the language of the Chaymas, and the
resemblance of sounds confuses the poor Indians and suggests
to them the most whimsical ideas. Of this I may cite an example. I saw a missionary laboring earnestly to prove that
infierno, hell, and *invierno,* winter, were not one and the same
thing, but as different as heat and cold. The Chaymas are
acquainted with no other winter than the season of rains, and
consequently they imagined the "Hell of the whites" to be a
place where the wicked are exposed to frequent showers. The
missionary harangued to no purpose. It was impossible to

efface the first impression produced by the analogy between the two consonants. He could not separate in the minds of the neophytes the ideas of rain and hell, invierno and infierno.

After passing almost the whole day in the open air, we employed our evenings at the convent in making notes, drying our plants, and sketching those that appeared to form new genera. Unfortunately, the misty atmosphere of a valley where the surrounding forests fill the air with an enormous quantity of vapor was unfavorable to astronomical observations. I spent a part of the nights waiting to take advantage of the moment when some star should be visible between the clouds near its passage over the meridian. . . . The instruments remained set up in the court of the convent for several hours, yet I was almost always disappointed in my expectations.

The vexation of seeing the stars disappear in a misty sky was the only disappointment we felt in the valley of Caripe. The aspect of this spot presents a character at once wild and tranquil, gloomy and attractive. In the solitude of these mountains we are perhaps less struck by the new impressions we receive at every step than with the marks of resemblance we trace in climates the most remote from each other. The hills by which the convent is backed are crowned with palm trees and tree-like ferns. In the evening, when the sky denotes rain, the air resounds with the monotonous howling of the howler monkeys, which resembles the distant sound of wind when it shakes the forest. Yet amid these strange sounds, these wild forms of plants, and these prodigies of a new world, nature everywhere speaks to man in a voice familiar to him. The turf that overspreads the soil, the old moss and fern that cover the roots of the trees, the torrents that gush down the sloping banks of the calcareous rocks, the harmonious accordance of tints reflected by the waters, the verdure, and the sky—everything recalls to the traveler sensations which he has already felt.

On September 22 Humboldt and Bonpland left the convent followed by four mules laden with their instruments and plants. When they finally returned to Cumaná, they had the opportunity to observe an eclipse of the sun, experience an earthquake, and watch a shower of meteorites that became famous in astronomy records.

AN ECLIPSE, AN EARTHQUAKE, AND A METEOR SHOWER

WE REMAINED a month longer at Cumaná, employing ourselves in the necessary preparations for our proposed visit to the Orinoco and the Río Negro. We had to choose such instruments as could be most easily transported in narrow boats, and to engage guides for an inland journey of ten months across a country without communication with the coasts.

On the 28th of October I was, at five in the morning, on the terrace of our house making preparations for the observation of the eclipse. The weather was fine and serene. The crescent of Venus and the constellation of the Ship, so splendid from the disposition of its immense nebulae, were lost in the rays of the rising sun. I had a complete observation of the progress and close of the eclipse. . . .

During a few days which preceded and followed the eclipse of the sun, very remarkable atmospherical phenomena were observable. It was what is called in those countries the season of winter—that is, of clouds and small electrical showers. From the 10th of October to the 3rd of November, at nightfall a reddish vapor arose on the horizon and in a few minutes covered the azure vault of the sky with a veil. . . .

On the 4th of November, about two in the afternoon, large clouds of peculiar blackness enveloped the high mountains of the Brigantine and the Tataraqual. They extended by degrees as far as the zenith. About four in the afternoon thunder was heard over our heads at an immense height, not regularly rolling but with a hollow and often interrupted sound. At the moment of the strongest electric explosion there were two shocks of earthquake.

The people ran into the streets, uttering loud cries. Bonpland, who was leaning over a table examining plants, was almost thrown on the floor. I felt the shock very strongly, though I was lying in a hammock. Its direction was from north to south, which is rare at Cumaná. Slaves, who were drawing water from a well more than eighteen or twenty feet deep near the Manzanares River, heard a noise like the explosion of a strong charge of gunpowder. The noise seemed to come from the bottom of the well—a very curious phenomenon, though very common in most of the countries of America which are exposed to earthquakes.

The sunset presented a picture of extraordinary magnificence. The thick veil of clouds was rent asunder as in shreds quite near the horizon. The sun appeared on a sky of indigo blue. Its disk was enormously enlarged, distorted and undulated towards the edges. The clouds were gilded, and clusters of divergent rays reflecting the most brilliant rainbow hues extended over the heavens. A great crowd of people assembled in the public square. This celestial phenomenon, the earthquake, the thunder which accompanied it, the red vapor seen during so many days, all were regarded as the effect of the eclipse. . . .

The earthquake of the 4th of November, the first I had felt, made the greater impression on me as it was accompanied with remarkable meteorological variations. It was, moreover, a positive movement upward and downward, and not a shock by undulation. I did not then imagine that after a long abode on the tablelands of Quito and the coasts of Peru I should become almost as familiar with the abrupt movements of the ground as we are in Europe with the sound of thunder. . . .

From our infancy the idea of certain contrasts becomes fixed in our minds. Water appears to us an element that moves, earth a motionless and inert mass. These impressions are the result of daily experience. They are connected with everything that is transmitted to us by the senses. When the shock of an earthquake is felt, when the earth which we had deemed so stable is shaken on its old foundations, one instant suffices to destroy long-fixed illusions. It is like awakening from a dream, but a painful awakening. We feel that we have been deceived by the apparent stability of nature. We become observant of the least noise. We mistrust for the first time the soil we have so long trod with confidence. But if the shocks be repeated, if they become frequent during several successive days, the uncertainty disappears. . . . Confidence easily springs up in the human breast. On the coasts of Peru we become accustomed to the undulations of the ground, as the sailor becomes accustomed to the tossing of the ship, caused by the motion of the waves. . . .

The night of the 11th of November was cool and extremely fine. From half after two in the morning the most extraordinary luminous meteors were seen in the direction of the east. Monsieur Bonpland, who had risen to enjoy the fresh-

ness of the air, perceived them first. Thousands of meteors
and falling stars succeeded each other during the space of four
hours. Their direction was very regular from north to
south. . . .

We did not neglect, during the course of our journey from
Caracas to the Río Negro [after they left Cumaná], to inquire
everywhere whether the meteors of the 12th of November had
been perceived. In a wild country, where the greater number
of the inhabitants sleep in the open air, so extraordinary a
phenomenon could not fail to be remarked unless it had been
concealed from observation by clouds.

The Capuchin missionary at San Fernando de Apure, a village situated amid the savannas of the province of Varinas,
the Franciscan monks stationed near the cataracts of the
Orinoco and at Maroa on the banks of the Río Negro had
seen numberless falling stars and meteors illumine the
heavens. All these observers compared the phenomenon to
brilliant fireworks, and it lasted from three till six in the
morning.

I was forcibly struck by the immense height which these
meteors must have attained, to have rendered them visible
simultaneously at Cumaná and on the frontiers of Brazil, in
a line six hundred and ninety miles in length. But what was
my astonishment when, on my return to Europe, I learned
that the same phenomenon had been perceived on an extent
of the globe of 64° of latitude and 91° of longitude—at the
equator in South America, at Labrador, and in Germany!

CHAPTER THREE

THE STEPPES OF SOUTH AMERICA

*On November 15, Humboldt and Bonpland left Cu-
maná and sailed along the coast to the port of La Guaira,
near the city of Caracas. They stayed there until the end
of the rainy season.*

*At the end of February, 1800, they set out across the
great plains, or* llanos, *of Venezuela, in the dry season an
area as arid and hot as the deserts of Africa.*

CROSSING THE LLANOS

IN THE Mesa de Paja, in the ninth degree of latitude, we entered the basin of the *llanos*. The sun was almost at its zenith;
the earth, wherever it appeared sterile and destitute of vegetation, was at the temperature of 118° to 122°F. Not a breath of
air was felt at the height at which we were on our mules; yet,
in the midst of this apparent calm, whirls of dust incessantly
arose. These were driven on by those small currents of air
which glide only over the surface of the ground and are caused
by the difference of temperature between the naked sand and
the spots covered with grass. These sand winds augment the
suffocating heat of the air. Every grain of quartz, hotter than
the surrounding air, radiates heat in every direction; and it is
difficult to observe the temperature of the atmosphere, owing
to these particles of sand striking against the bulb of the ther-

mometer. All around us the plains seemed to ascend to the sky, and the vast and profound solitude appeared like an ocean covered with seaweed. The horizon in some places was clear and distinct; in others it appeared undulating, sinuous, and as if striped. The earth there was confounded with the sky. Through the dry mist and strata of vapor the trunks of palm trees were seen from afar, stripped of their foliage and their verdant summits and looking like the masts of a ship descried upon the horizon.

There is something awful, as well as sad and gloomy, in the uniform aspect of these steppes. Everything seems motionless; scarcely does a small cloud, passing across the zenith and denoting the approach of the rainy season, cast its shadow on the earth. . . .

The llanos and the pampas of South America are really steppes. They are covered with beautiful vegetation in the rainy season, but in the time of great drought they assume the aspect of a desert. The grass is then reduced to powder; the earth cracks; the alligators and the great serpents remain buried in the dried mud till awakened from their long lethargy by the first showers of spring. . . .

The chief characteristic of the savannas or steppes of South America is the absolute want of hills and inequalities—the perfect level of every part of the soil. Accordingly, the Spanish conquerors who first penetrated from Coro to the banks of the Apure did not call them deserts or savannas or meadows, but plains (llanos). Often within a distance of two or three hundred square miles there is not an eminence a foot high. . . .

The uniform landscape of the llanos; the extremely small number of their inhabitants; the fatigue of traveling beneath a burning sky and an atmosphere darkened by dust; the view of that horizon which seems forever to fly before us; those lonely trunks of palm trees, which have all the same aspect, and which we despair of reaching because they are confounded with other trunks that rise by degrees on the visual horizon— all these causes combine to make the steppes appear far more extensive than they are in reality. . . .

After having passed two nights on horseback and sought in vain by day for some shelter from the heat of the sun beneath the tufts of the Mauritia [fan] palm trees, we arrived before night at the little Hato del Cayman [Farm of the Alligator], called also La Guadaloupe. It was a solitary house in the steppes, surrounded by a few small huts covered with reeds and skins. The cattle, oxen, horses, and mules are not penned, but wander freely over an extent of several square leagues. There is nowhere any enclosure; men, naked to the waist and armed with a lance, ride over the savannas to inspect the animals, bringing back those that wander too far from the pastures of the farm, and branding all that do not already bear the mark of their proprietor. These mulattoes, who are known by the name of *peones llaneros,* are partly freedmen and partly slaves. They are constantly exposed to the burning heat of the tropical sun. Their food is meat, dried in the air and a little salted; and of this even their horses sometimes partake. Being always in the saddle, they fancy they cannot make the slightest excursion on foot.

We found an old Negro slave who managed the farm in the absence of his master. He told us of herds composed of several thousand cows that were grazing in the steppes; yet we asked in vain for a bowl of milk. We were offered in a calabash some yellow, muddy, and fetid water drawn from a neighboring pool. The indolence of the inhabitants of the llanos is such that they do not dig wells, though they know that almost everywhere, at ten feet deep, fine springs are found in a stratum of conglomerate, or red sandstone. After suffering during one half of the year from the effect of inundations, they quietly resign themselves during the other half to the most distressing deprivation of water. The old Negro advised us to cover the cup with a linen cloth and drink as through a filter, that we might not be incommoded by the smell and might swallow less of the yellowish mud suspended in the water. We did not then think that we should afterward be forced, during whole months, to have recourse to this expedient. The waters of the Orinoco are always loaded with earthy particles; they are even putrid where dead bodies of alligators are found in the creeks lying on banks of sand or half buried in the mud.

No sooner were our instruments unloaded and safely placed than our mules were set at liberty to, as they say here, *para buscar agua*—that is, "to search for water." There are little pools around the farm, which the animals find, guided by their instinct, by the view of some scattered tufts of Mauritia palms, and by the sensation of humid coolness caused by little currents of air amid an atmosphere which to us appears calm and tranquil. . . .

We followed our mules in search of one of those pools whence the muddy water had been drawn that so ill quenched our thirst. We were covered with dust and tanned by the sandy wind which burns the skin even more than the rays of the sun. We longed impatiently to take a bath, but we found only a great pool of foul water surrounded with palm trees. The water was turbid, though, to our great astonishment, a little cooler than the air. Accustomed during our long journey to bathe whenever we had an opportunity, often several times in one day, we hastened to plunge into the pool. We had scarcely begun to enjoy the coolness of the bath when a noise which we heard on the opposite bank made us leave the water precipitately. It was an alligator plunging into the mud.

In order to escape as much as possible from the heat of the day, we set off at two in the morning with the hope of reaching Calabozo before noon, a small but busy trading town situated in the midst of the llanos. The aspect of the country was still the same. There was no moonlight; but the great masses of nebulae that spot the southern sky enlighten, as they set, a part of the terrestrial horizon. The solemn spectacle of the starry vault, seen in its immense expanse; the cool breeze which blows over the plain during the night; the waving motion of the grass wherever it has attained any height—everything recalled to our minds the surface of the ocean. The illusion was augmented when the disk of the sun appearing on the horizon repeated its image by the effects of refraction and, soon losing its flattened form, ascended rapidly and straight towards the zenith. . . .

In proportion as the sun rose towards the zenith and the earth and the strata of superincumbent air took different temperatures, the phenomenon of the mirage displayed itself in its numerous modifications. . . . The little currents of air that swept the surface of the soil had so variable a temperature that, in a drove of wild oxen, one part appeared with the legs raised above the surface of the ground, while the other rested on it. . . .

On the way across the llanos they had an opportunity to study electric eels. In Europe, Humboldt had done many experiments on the effect of electricity on nerves and muscles. Now here, in the backwaters of South America, was a fish that gave off powerful currents of real electricity.

In many marine aquariums today you can see and hear the powerful electric discharges of electric eels. The high voltage given off paralyzes other fishes and frogs on which the eels feed. Humboldt himself received painful shocks when he performed his pioneer experiments on the electric eels around Calabozo.

ELECTRIC EELS

I WAS impatient, from the time of my arrival at Cumaná, to procure electric eels. We had been promised them often, but our hopes had always been disappointed. . . .

In the llanos, particularly in the environs of Calabozo, the basins of stagnant water and the confluents of the Orinoco are filled with electric eels. We at first wished to make our experiments in the house we inhabited at Calabozo, but the dread of the shocks caused by the *gymnoti* [electric eels] is so great, and so exaggerated among the common people, that during three days we could not obtain one, though they are easily caught and we had promised the Indians two piastres for every strong and vigorous fish. This fear of the Indians is the more extraordinary as they do not attempt to adopt precautions in which they profess to have great confidence. When interrogated on the effect of the *tembladores* [electric fish], they never fail to tell the whites that they may be touched with impunity while you are chewing tobacco. . . .

Impatient of waiting, and having obtained very uncertain results from an electric eel which had been brought to us alive but much enfeebled, we repaired to the Caño de Bera [a stream] to make our experiments in the open air and at the edge of the water. We set off on the 19th of March, at a very early hour, for the village of Rastro. From there we were conducted by the Indians to a stream which in the time of drought forms a basin of muddy water surrounded by fine trees.

To catch the gymnoti with nets is very difficult on account of the extreme agility of the fish, which bury themselves in the mud. We would not employ roots which, thrown into the pool, intoxicate or benumb the eels. These methods have the effect of enfeebling the gymnoti. The Indians therefore told us that they would "fish with horses." We found it difficult to form an idea of this extraordinary manner of fishing, but we soon saw our guides return from the savanna, which they had been scouring for wild horses and mules. They brought about thirty with them, which they forced to enter the pool.

The extraordinary noise caused by the horses' hoofs makes the fish issue from the mud and excites them to the attack. These yellowish and livid eels, resembling large aquatic serpents, swim on the surface of the water and crowd under the bellies of the horses and mules. A contest between animals of so different an organization presents a very striking spectacle. The Indians, provided with harpoons and long slender reeds, surround the pool closely, and some climb up the trees, the branches of which extend horizontally over the surface of the water. By their wild cries and the length of their reeds, they prevent the horses from running away and reaching the bank of the pool. The eels, stunned by the noise, defend themselves by the repeated discharge of their electric batteries. For a long interval they seem likely to prove victorious. Several horses sink beneath the violence of the invisible strokes which they receive from all sides. . . . Stunned by the force and frequency

HORSES BEING ATTACKED BY ELECTRIC EELS

of the shocks, they disappear under the water. Others, panting, with manes erect and haggard eyes expressing anguish and dismay, raise themselves and endeavor to flee from the storm by which they are overtaken. They are driven back by the Indians into the middle of the water, but a small number succeed in eluding the active vigilance of the fishermen. These regain the shore, stumbling at every step, and stretch themselves on the sand, exhausted with fatigue, and with limbs benumbed by the electric shocks of the gymnoti.

In less than five minutes two of our horses were drowned. The eel, being five feet long and pressing itself against the belly of the horses, makes a discharge along the whole extent of its electric organ. It attacks at once the heart, the intestines, and . . . the abdominal nerves. The horses are probably not killed but only stunned. They are drowned from the impossibility of rising amid the prolonged struggle between the other horses and the eels.

We had little doubt that the fishing would terminate by killing successively all the animals engaged, but by degrees the impetuosity of this unequal combat diminished and the wearied gymnoti dispersed. They require a long rest and abundant nourishment to repair the [electrical] force which they have lost. The mules and horses appear less frightened; their manes are no longer bristled, and their eyes express less dread. The gymnoti approach timidly the edge of the marsh, where they are taken by means of small harpoons fastened to long cords. When the cords are very dry, the Indians feel no shock in raising the fish into the air. In a few minutes we had five large eels, most of which were but slightly wounded. Some others were taken by the same means towards evening. . . .

It would be temerity to expose ourselves to the first shocks of a very large and strongly irritated gymnotus. If by chance a stroke be received before the fish is wounded or wearied by long pursuit, the pain and numbness are so violent that it is impossible to describe the nature of the feeling they excite. I do not remember having ever received from the discharge of a large Leyden jar a more dreadful shock than that which I experienced by imprudently placing both my feet on a gymnotus just taken out of the water. I was affected during the rest of the day with a violent pain in the knees and in almost every joint. . . .

We often tried, both insulated and otherwise, to touch the fish without feeling the least shock. When Bonpland held it by the head or by the middle of the body while I held it by the tail and, standing on the moist ground, did not take each other's hand, one of us received shocks which the other did not feel. It depends upon the gymnotus to direct its action towards the point where it finds itself most strongly irritated. . . .

The gymnoti, which are objects of curiosity and of the deepest interest to the philosophers of Europe, are at once dreaded and detested by the natives. They furnish, indeed, in their muscular flesh, pretty good food; but the electric organ fills the greater part of their body, and this organ is slimy and disagreeable to the taste; it is accordingly separated with care from the rest of the eel. The presence of gymnoti is also considered as the principal cause of the want of fish in the ponds and pools of the llanos. They, however, kill many more than they devour, and the Indians told us that when young alligators and gymnoti are caught at the same time in very strong nets, the latter never show the slightest trace of a wound, because they disable the young alligators before they are attacked by them. All the inhabitants of the waters dread the society of the gymnoti. Lizards, tortoises, and frogs seek pools where they are secure from the electric action. It became necessary to change the direction of a road near Uritucu because the electric eels were so numerous in one river that every year they killed a great number of mules as they forded the water with their burdens.

Though in the present state of our knowledge we may flatter ourselves with having thrown some light on the extraordinary effects of electric fishes, yet a vast number of physical and physiological researches still remain to be made. . . . It will perhaps be found that in most animals every contraction of the muscular fiber is preceded by a discharge from the nerve into the muscle, and that the mere simple contact of heterogeneous substances is a source of movement and of life in all organized beings.

CROCODILES AND BATS

WE LEFT the town of Calabozo on the 24th of March, highly satisfied with our stay and the experiments we had made on an object so worthy of the attention of physiologists. I had besides obtained some good observations of the stars and discovered with surprise that the errors of maps amounted here also to a quarter of a degree of latitude. No person had taken an observation before me on this spot. . . .

As we advanced into the southern part of the llanos we found the ground more dusty, more destitute of herbage, and more cracked by the effect of long drought. The palm trees disappeared by degrees. The thermometer kept from eleven in the morning till sunset at about 95°[F]. . . .

During the night we forded the Río Uritucu, which abounds with a breed of crocodiles remarkable for their ferocity. We were advised to prevent our dogs from going to drink in the rivers, for it often happens that the crocodiles of Uritucu come out of the water and pursue dogs upon the shore. This intrepidity is so much the more striking as twenty-four miles away the crocodiles of the Río Tisnao are extremely timid and little dangerous. The manners of animals vary in the same species according to local circumstances difficult to be determined.

We were shown a hut or, rather, a kind of shed in which our host of Calabozo, Don Miguel Cousin, had witnessed a very extraordinary scene. Sleeping with one of his friends on a bench or couch covered with leather, Don Miguel was awakened early in the morning by a violent shaking and a horrible noise. Clods of earth were thrown into the middle of the hut. Presently a young crocodile two or three feet long issued from under the bed, darted at a dog which lay on the threshold of the door, and, missing him in the impetuosity of his spring, ran towards the beach to gain the river. On examining the spot where the *barbacoa,* or couch, was placed, the cause of this strange adventure was easily discovered. The ground was disturbed to a considerable depth. It was dried mud, which had covered the crocodile in that state of lethargy, or summer sleep, in which many of the species lie during the absence of the rains in the llanos. The noise of men and horses, perhaps the smell of the dog, had aroused the crocodile. The hut being built at the edge of the pool and inundated during part of the year, the crocodile had no doubt entered, at the time of the inundation of the savannas, by the same opening at which it was seen to go out. The Indians often find enormous boas,

which they call *uji*, or water serpents, in the same lethargic
state. To reanimate them, they must be irritated or wetted
with water. Boas are killed and immersed in the streams to
obtain, by means of putrefaction, the tendons of the dorsal
muscles, of which excellent guitar strings are made at Calabozo, preferable to those furnished by the intestines of the
alouate [howling] monkeys.

The drought and heat of the llanos act like cold upon animals and plants. Beyond the tropics the trees lose their leaves
in a very dry air. Reptiles, particularly crocodiles and boas,
having very indolent habits, leave with reluctance the basins
in which they have found water at the period of great inundations. In proportion as the pools become dry, these animals
penetrate into the mud to seek that degree of humidity which
gives flexibility to their skin and integuments. In this state of
repose they are seized with stupefaction; but possibly they preserve a communication with the external air. . . .

We passed the Guarico and encamped in the savannas south
of Guayaval. Enormous bats hovered as usual over our hammocks during a great part of the night. Every moment they
seemed to be about to fasten on our faces. Early in the morning
we pursued our way over low grounds, often inundated. In the
season of rains a boat may be navigated as on a lake between
the Guarico and the Apure. We arrived on the 27th of March
at the Villa de San Fernando, the capital of the mission of the
Capuchins in the province of Varinas. This was the termina-
tion of our journey over the llanos, for we passed the three
months of April, May, and June [1800] on the rivers.

CHAPTER FOUR

DOWN THE APURE RIVER

Humboldt and Bonpland knew that they were setting out on a long, difficult, and dangerous journey when they reached the Apure River. Indian canoes were not the safest of crafts. There were great rapids to pass. Wild animals and unfriendly, perhaps cannibal Indians might be encountered. There was the ever present possibility of dreaded tropical fevers that had taken the lives of previous explorers of the jungles of Venezuela.

But the stakes were high. There was rich new vegetation to collect and classify—hundreds, even thousands of plants unknown to European botanists. Would these plants be related to those already known in other parts of the world or be members of completely unknown families? There were certain to be insects, birds, animals, reptiles, and fish never before studied by zoologists.

And what were the people of such tropical jungles like? Humboldt wanted to see them and to learn as much of their languages, customs, and beliefs as possible. Few scientifically trained people had observed savages and come to know them in their normal surroundings.

Humboldt also planned to use his especially fine compasses to study the earth's magnetism. Ever since Columbus' first voyage it had been known that the compass did not always point to the true north. We know now that this is because the earth is a gigantic magnet whose poles are about 1,400 miles from the geographic poles. By Humboldt's time there was a lot of evidence that in different parts of the earth the compass needles veered farther away from the north than in other places. The earth's lines of magnetic force spread from the poles, but they form irregular bands over it. Humboldt was interested in this subject and took compass readings wherever he went. He was particularly concerned with what he would observe as they drew near the equator.

But the biggest challenge of all, perhaps, came from the long dispute as to whether the Orinoco and the Amazon rivers were joined by others into one great waterway that linked the northeast coast of Venezuela near the Caribbean Sea with the mouths of the Amazon on the Atlantic Ocean a thousand miles away.

Their plan was to follow the Apure into the Orinoco, ascend the Orinoco to its tributary the Atabapo, then follow smaller rivers to where a short portage would take them to the Río Negro, which was known to flow into the Amazon. Then they could go up the Casiquiare, rejoin the Orinoco, and return entirely by water. This would prove beyond any possible doubt that a direct connection existed between the Orinoco and the Amazon. The challenge was similar to that of the North Americans who first explored the connections between the Mississippi and the Ohio and Missouri river systems.

With their sextants they could determine the latitude of every place they stopped, and with their chronometer (an especially exact clock which they kept on Greenwich time) they could find the longitude. Their barometers would give them the altitude above sea level of every point they passed, and their thermometers the temperature.

*The compasses would determine the angle of every bend
in the rivers they traversed. With these instruments the
travelers would be able to make the first complete and
exact map of the Orinoco and its tributaries.*

*Humboldt and Bonpland looked forward to the adven-
tures before them in this wild and little-known section of
tropical America.*

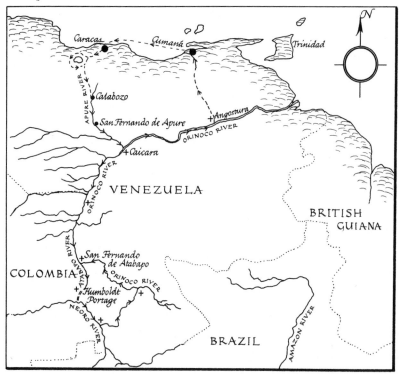

ROUTE DOWN THE ORINOCO

JUST AS IN PARADISE

WE CHOSE one of those very large canoes called *lanchas* by the
Spaniards. A pilot and four Indians were sufficient to manage
it. They constructed near the stern, in the space of a few hours,

a cabin covered with palm leaves, sufficiently spacious to contain a table and benches. These were made of ox hides strained tight and nailed to frames of brazilwood. I mention these minute circumstances to prove that our accommodations on the Río Apure were far different from those to which we were afterwards reduced in the narrow boats of the Orinoco.

We loaded the canoe with provisions for a month. Fowls, eggs, plantains, cassavas, and [cocoa beans] are found in abundance at San Fernando. The good Capuchin, Friar José María de Málaga, gave us sherry wine, oranges, and tamarinds to make cooling beverages. We could easily foresee that a roof constructed of palm-tree leaves would become excessively hot on a large river, where we were almost always exposed to the perpendicular rays of the sun. The Indians relied less on the provisions we had purchased than on their hooks and nets. We also took some firearms, which we found in general use as far as the cataracts; but farther south the great humidity of the air prevents the missionaries from using them.

The Río Apure abounds in fish, manatees [large water mammals], and turtles, the eggs of which afford a food more nutritious than agreeable to the taste. Its banks are inhabited by an innumerable quantity of birds, among which *pauxi* and the *guacharaca,* which may be called the turkeys and pheasants of those countries, are found to be most useful. . . .

During the whole of my voyage from San Fernando de Apure to San Carlos del Río Negro and thence to the town of Angostura [now Ciudad Bolívar], I noted down day by day, either in the boat or where we disembarked at night, all that appeared to me worthy of observation. Violent rains and the prodigious quantity of mosquitoes with which the air is filled on the banks of the Orinoco and the Casiquiare necessarily occasioned some interruptions; but I supplied the omission by notes taken a few days after. . . .

Having passed the Diamante [island], we entered a land inhabited by tigers, crocodiles, and *chiguires* [capybaras or water hogs]. . . . The river widens by degrees. One of its banks is generally barren and sandy from the effect of inundations; the other is higher and covered with lofty trees. In some parts, the river is bordered by forests on each side and forms a straight canal 960 feet broad. The manner in which the trees are disposed is very remarkable. We first find bushes of *sauso* forming a kind of hedge four feet high and appearing as if they had been clipped by the hand of man. A thicket of cedar, brazilletto, and lignum-vitae trees rises behind this hedge.

The large quadrupeds of those regions, the jaguars, tapirs, and peccaries, have made openings in the hedge of sauso which we have just described. Through these the wild animals pass when they come to drink at the river. As they fear but little the approach of a boat, we had the pleasure of viewing them as they paced slowly along the shore until they disappeared in the forest, which they entered by one of the narrow passes left at intervals between the bushes. These scenes, which were often repeated, had ever for me a peculiar attraction. The pleasure they excite is not owing solely to the interest which the naturalist takes in the objects of his study; it is connected with a feeling common to all men who have been brought up in the habits of civilization. You find yourself in a new world, in the midst of untamed and savage nature. Now the jaguar, the beautiful panther of America, appears upon the shore; and now the *hocco* (peacock-pheasant), with its black plumage and tufted head, moves slowly along the sausos. Animals of the most different classes succeed each other. "Esse como en el

CROCODILE AND JAGUAR

Paradiso"—"It is just as it was in Paradise"—said our pilot, an old Indian of the missions. . . .

When the shore is of considerable breadth, the hedge of sauso remains at a distance from the river. In the intermediate space we see crocodiles, sometimes to the number of eight or ten, stretched on the sand. Motionless, with their jaws wide open, they repose by each other without displaying any of those marks of affection observed in other animals living in society. The troop separates as soon as they quit the shore. It is, however, probably composed of one male only and many females; for, as Monsieur Descourtils, who has so much studied the crocodiles of St. Domingo, observed to me, the males are rare, because they kill one another in fighting during the season of their loves.

These monstrous creatures are so numerous that throughout the whole course of the river we had at almost every instant five or six in view. Yet at this period the swelling of the Río Apure was scarcely perceived, and, consequently, hundreds of crocodiles were still buried in the mud of the savannas. . . . The Indians told us that at San Fernando de Apure scarcely a year passes without two or three grownup persons, particularly women who fetch water from the river, being drowned by these carnivorous reptiles. They related to us the history of a young girl of Uritucu who by singular intrepidity and presence of mind saved herself from the jaws of a crocodile. When she felt herself seized, she sought the eyes of the animal and plunged her fingers into them with such violence that the pain forced the crocodile to let her go after having bitten off the lower part of her left arm. The girl, notwithstanding the enormous quantity of blood she lost, reached the shore, swimming with the hand that still remained to her.

In those desert countries, where man is ever wrestling with nature, discourse daily turns on the best means that may be employed to escape from a tiger, a boa, or a crocodile. Everyone prepares himself in some sort for the dangers that may await him. "I know," said the young girl of Uritucu coolly, "that the cayman lets go his hold if you push your fingers into his eyes." Long after my return to Europe I learned that in the interior of Africa the Negroes know and practice the same means of defense.

ANIMAL LIFE ALONG THE APURE

THE CROCODILES of the Apure find abundant food in the *chiguires,* which live fifty or sixty together in troops on the banks of the river. These animals, as large as our pigs, have no weapons of defense; they swim somewhat better than they run, yet they become the prey of the crocodiles in the water and of the tigers on land. It is difficult to conceive how, being thus persecuted by two powerful enemies, they become so numerous; but they breed with the same rapidity as the little *cavies,* or guinea pigs, which come to us from Brazil. . . .

Near the *Joval* [a bend of the river] nature assumes an awful and extremely wild aspect. We there saw the largest jaguar we had ever met with. The natives themselves were astonished at its prodigious length, which surpassed that of any Bengal tiger I had ever seen in the museums of Europe. The animal lay stretched beneath the shade of a large mimosa. It had just killed a chiguire, but had not yet touched its prey, on which it kept one of its paws. The zamuro vultures were assembled in great numbers to devour the remains of the jaguar's repast. They presented the most curious spectacle, by a singular mixture of boldness and timidity. They advanced to within two

feet of the animal, but at the least movement he made they
drew back. In order to observe more nearly the manners of
these creatures we went into the little skiff that accompanied
our canoe. Tigers very rarely attack boats by swimming to
them, and never but when their ferocity is heightened by a
long privation of food. The noise of our oars led the animal to
rise slowly and hide itself behind the sauso bushes that bordered the shore. The vultures tried to profit by this moment of
absence to devour the chiguire; but the tiger, notwithstanding
the proximity of our boat, leaped into the midst of them and in
a fit of rage, expressed by his gait and the movement of his
tail, carried off his prey to the forest. The Indians regretted
that they were not provided with their lances in order to go on
shore and attack the tiger. They are accustomed to this weapon
and were right in not trusting to our firearms. In so excessively
damp an atmosphere, muskets often misfire.

Continuing to descend the river, we met with the great herd
of chiguires which the tiger had put to flight and from which
he had selected his prey. These animals saw us land very un-
concernedly; some of them were seated and gazed upon us,
moving the upper lip like rabbits. They seemed not to be
afraid of man, but the sight of our dog put them to flight.
Their hind legs being longer than their fore legs, their pace
is a slight gallop, but with so little swiftness that we succeeded
in catching two of them. The chiguire, which swims with the
greatest agility, utters a short moan in running as if its respira-
tion were impeded. It is the largest of the family of rodents, or
gnawing animals. It defends itself only at the last extremity
when it is surrounded and wounded. Having great strength in
its grinding teeth—particularly the hinder ones, which are

pretty long—it can tear the paw of a tiger or the leg of a horse with its bite.

JUNGLE SERENADE

BEYOND THE Vuelta del Cochina Roto, in a spot where the river has scooped itself a new bed, we passed the night on a bare and very extensive strand. The forest being impenetrable, we had the greatest difficulty to find dry wood to light fires, near which the Indians believe themselves in safety from the nocturnal attacks of the tiger. . . .

The night was calm and serene and there was a beautiful moonlight. The crocodiles, stretched along the shore, placed themselves in such a manner as to be able to see the fire. We thought we observed that its blaze attracted them as it attracts fishes, crayfish, and other inhabitants of the water. The Indians showed us the tracks of three tigers in the sand, two of which were very young. A female had no doubt conducted her little ones to drink at the river. Finding no tree on the strand, we stuck our oars in the ground and to these we fastened our hammocks.

Everything passed tranquilly till eleven at night. Then a noise so terrific arose in the neighboring forest that it was almost impossible to close our eyes. Amid the cries of so many wild beasts howling at once, the Indians discriminated such only as were at intervals heard separately. These were the little soft cries of the sapajou monkeys, the moans of the alouate apes, the howlings of the jaguar and cougar, the peccary and the sloth, and the cries of the curassow, the parraka, and other [chicken-like] birds. When the jaguars approached the skirt of the forest, our dog, which till then had never ceased barking,

Down the Apure River

began to howl and seek for shelter beneath our hammocks. Sometimes, after a long silence, the cry of the tiger came from the tops of the trees, and then it was followed by the sharp and long whistling of the monkeys, which appeared to flee from the danger that threatened them. We heard the same noises repeated during the course of whole months, whenever the forest approached the bed of the river. The security evinced by the Indians inspires confidence in the minds of travelers, who readily persuade themselves that the tigers are afraid of fire and that they do not attack a man lying in his hammock. These attacks are in fact extremely rare. During a long abode in South America I remember only one example of a llanero who was found mutilated in his hammock opposite the island of Achaguas.

When the natives are interrogated on the causes of the tremendous noise made by the beasts of the forest at certain hours of the night, the answer is, "They are keeping the feast of the full moon."

I believe this agitation is most frequently the effect of some conflict that has arisen in the depths of the forest. The jaguars, for instance, pursue the peccaries and the tapirs, which, having no defense but in their numbers, flee in close troops and break down the bushes they find in their way. Terrified at this struggle, the timid and mistrustful monkeys answer, from the tops of the trees, the cries of the large animals. They awaken the birds that live in society, and by degrees the whole assembly is in commotion. It is not always in a fine moonlight, but more particularly at the time of a storm and violent showers that this tumult takes place among the wild beasts. "May heaven grant them a quiet night and repose, and us also!" said the monk who accompanied us to the Río Negro when, sinking with fatigue, he assisted in arranging our accommodations for the night. It was indeed strange to find no silence in the solitude of the woods. In the inns of Spain we dread the sound of guitars from the next apartment. On the Orinoco, where the traveler's resting place is the open beach or beneath the shelter of a solitary tree, his slumbers are disturbed by a serenade from the forest.   •

THE CANNIBAL FISH

SINCE OUR departure from San Fernando [de Apure] we had not met a single boat on this fine river. Everything denotes the most profound solitude. On the morning of the 3rd of April our Indians caught with a hook the fish known in the country by the name of *caribe* [piranha], meaning "cannibal," because no other fish has such a thirst for blood. It attacks bathers and swimmers, from whom it often bites away considerable pieces of flesh. The Indians dread these caribes extremely. Several of them showed us the scars of deep wounds in the calf of the leg and in the thigh made by these little animals. They swim at the bottom of rivers; but if a few drops of blood be shed on the water they rise by thousands to the surface, so that if a person be only slightly bitten it is difficult for him to get out of the water without receiving a severer wound. When we reflect on the numbers of these fish, the largest and most voracious of which are only four or five inches long, on the triangular form of their sharp and cutting teeth, and on the amplitude of their retractile mouths, we need not be surprised at the fear which the caribe excites in the inhabitants of the banks of the Apure and the Orinoco.

In places where the river was very limpid, where not a fish appeared, we threw into the water little morsels of raw flesh,

and in a few minutes a perfect cloud of caribes had come to
dispute their prey. . . . As no one dares to bathe where it [the
caribe] is found, it may be considered as one of the greatest
scourges of those climates in which the sting of the mosquitoes
and the general irritation of the skin render the use of baths
so necessary.

NO TIGER EVER LOOKED SO LARGE

WE STOPPED at noon in a deserted spot called Algodonal. I left
my companions while they drew the boat ashore and were occupied in preparing our dinner. I went along the beach to get
a new view of a group of crocodiles sleeping in the sun and
lying in such a manner as to have their tails, which were furnished with broad plates, resting on one another. Some little
herons, white as snow, walked along their backs and even upon
their heads, as if passing over trunks of trees. The crocodiles
were of a greenish gray, half covered with dried mud; from
their color and immobility they might have been taken for
statues of bronze.

This excursion nearly proved fatal to me. I had kept my
eyes constantly turned towards the river, but while picking up
some spangles of mica agglomerated together in the sand, I
discovered the recent footsteps of a tiger, easily distinguished
by their form and size. The animal had gone towards the forest,
and, turning my eyes on that side, I found myself within eighty
paces of a jaguar that was lying under the thick foliage of a
ceiba. No tiger had ever appeared to me so large.

There are accidents in life against which we may seek in
vain to fortify our reason. I was extremely alarmed, yet sufficient master of myself and of my motions to enable me to follow the advice which the Indians had so often given us as to

how we ought to act in such cases. I continued to walk on without running, avoided moving my arms, and I thought I observed the jaguar's attention was fixed on a herd of capybaras which was crossing the river. I then began to return, making a large circuit towards the edge of the water. As the distance increased I thought I might accelerate my pace. How often was I tempted to look back in order to assure myself that I was not pursued! Happily, I yielded very tardily to this desire. The jaguar had remained motionless. These enormous cats with spotted robes are so well fed in countries abounding in capybaras, peccaries, and deer that they rarely attack men. I arrived at the boat out of breath and related my adventure to the Indians. They appeared very little interested in my story; yet, after having loaded our guns, they accompanied us to the ceiba beneath which the jaguar had lain. He was there no longer, and it would have been imprudent to have pursued him into the forest, where we must have dispersed or advanced in single file amidst the intertwining lianas.

REACHING THE ORINOCO: GNATS AND BATS

THE 4TH of April was the last day we passed on the Río Apure. The vegetation of its bank became more and more uniform. During several days, and particularly since we had left the mission of Arichuna, we had suffered cruelly from the stings of insects which covered our faces and hands. They were not mosquitoes, which have the appearance of little flies, but *zancudos,* which are really gnats, though very different from our European species. These insects appear only after sunset. Their proboscis [tubular extension of the mouth] is so long that when they fix on the lower surface of a hammock, they pierce through it and the thickest garments with their sting.

We had intended to pass the night at the Vuelta del Palmito, but the number of jaguars at that part of the Apure is so great that our Indians found two hidden behind the trunk of a locust tree at the moment when they were going to sling our hammocks. We were advised to re-embark and take our station on the island of Apurito, near its junction with the Orinoco. That portion of the island belongs to the province of Caracas, while the right banks of the Apure and the Orinoco form a part, the one of the province of Varinas, the other of Spanish Guiana. We found no trees to which we could suspend our hammocks and were obliged to sleep on ox hides spread on the ground. The boats were too narrow and too full of gnats to permit us to pass the night in them. . . .

We touched several times on shoals before we entered the Orinoco. . . . It was not without emotion that we beheld for the first time, after long expectation, the waters of the Orinoco at a point so distant from the coast.

CHAPTER FIVE

THE ORINOCO RIVER

A PLACE OF SOLITUDE

ON LEAVING the Río Apure we found ourselves in a country presenting a totally different aspect. An immense plain of water stretched before us like a lake, as far as we could see. White-topped waves rose to the height of several feet, from the conflict of the breeze and the current. The air resounded no longer with the piercing cries of herons, flamingoes and spoonbills crossing in long files from one shore to the other. . . . All nature appeared less animated. . . . The horizon was bounded by a zone of forests, which nowhere reached so far as the bed of the river. A vast beach, constantly parched by the heat of the sun, desert and bare as the shores of the sea, resembled at a distance, from the effect of the mirage, pools of stagnant water. . . . In these scattered features of the landscape, in this character of solitude and greatness, we recognize the course of the Orinoco, one of the most majestic rivers of the New World. . . .

CARIB INDIANS

IN THE port of Encaramada we met with some Caribs of Panapana. A cacique [chief] was going up the Orinoco in his canoe to join in the famous fishing of turtle eggs. His canoe was rounded toward the bottom like a *bongo* [drum] and followed

by a smaller boat called a *curiara*. He was seated beneath a sort
of tent, constructed, like the sail, of palm leaves. His cold and
silent gravity, the respect with which he was treated by his at-
tendants—everything denoted him to be a person of importance. He was equipped, however, in the same manner as his
Indians. They were all equally naked, armed with bows and
arrows. The chief, the domestics, the furniture, the boat, and
the sail were all painted red.

These Caribs are men of an almost athletic stature; they appeared to us much taller than any Indians we had hitherto
seen. Their smooth and thick hair, cut short on the forehead
like that of choristers, their eyebrows painted black, their look
at once gloomy and animated gave a singular expression to
their countenances. . . . The women, who were very tall, and
disgusting from their want of cleanliness, carried their infants
on their backs. The thighs and legs of the infants were bound
at certain distances by broad strips of cotton cloth, and the
flesh, strongly compressed beneath the ligatures, was swelled
in the interstices. It is generally to be observed that the Caribs
are as attentive to their exterior and their ornaments as it is
possible for men to be who are naked and painted red. They
attach great importance to certain configurations of the body;
and a mother would be accused of culpable indifference toward
her children if she did not employ artificial means to shape the
calf of the leg after the fashion of the country. As none of our
Indians of Apure understood the Caribbee language, we could
obtain no information from the chief respecting the encamp-
ments that are made at this season in several islands of the
Orinoco for collecting turtle eggs. . . .

On the 6th of April, whilst continuing to ascend the Ori-

noco, first southward and then to southwest, we perceived the
southern side of the *Serrania,* or chain of the mountains of
Encaramada. . . .

LEGEND OF THE FLOOD

I CANNOT quit this first link of the mountains of Encaramada
without recalling to mind a fact that was often mentioned to
me during our abode in the missions of the Orinoco. The
natives of those countries have retained the belief that "at the
time of the great waters, when their fathers were forced to
have recourse to boats to escape the general inundation, the
waves of the sea beat against the rocks of Encaramada." This
belief is not confined to only one nation, the Tamanacs. It
makes part of a system of historical tradition, of which we find
scattered notions among the Maypures of the great cataracts;
among the Indians of the Río Erevato, which runs into the
Caura; and among almost all the tribes of the upper Orinoco.
When the Tamanacs are asked how the human race survived
this great deluge, they say, "A man and a woman saved themselves on a high mountain, called Tamanacu, situated on
the banks of the Asiveru; and, casting behind them, over
their heads, the fruits of the Mauritia palm tree, they saw the
seeds contained in those fruits produce men and women, who
repeopled the earth. . . ."

A few leagues from Encaramada a rock called *Tepu-me-
reme,* or "the painted rock," rises in the midst of the savanna. Upon it are traced representations of animals and
symbolic figures resembling those we saw in going down the
Orinoco at a small distance below Encaramada. . . . These
hieroglyphic figures are often seen at great heights on rocky
cliffs which could be accessible only by constructing very

lofty scaffolds. When the natives are asked how those figures could have been sculptured, they answer with a smile, as if relating a fact of which only a white man could be ignorant, that at the period of the great waters their fathers went to that height in boats.

These ancient traditions of the human race, which we find dispersed over the whole surface of the globe, like the relics of a vast shipwreck, are highly interesting in the philosophical study of our own species. Like certain families of the vegetable kingdom which, notwithstanding the diversity of climates and the influence of heights, retain the impression of a common type, the traditions of nations respecting the origin of the world display everywhere the same physiognomy and preserve features of resemblance that fill us with astonishment. How many different tongues, belonging to branches that appear totally distinct, transmit to us the same facts! The traditions concerning races that have been destroyed and the renewal of nature scarcely vary in reality, though every nation gives them a local coloring. In the great continents, as in the smallest islands of the Pacific Ocean, it is always on the loftiest and nearest mountain that the remains of the human race have been saved; and this even appears the more recent in proportion as the nations are uncultivated, and as the knowledge they have of their own existence has no very remote date.

THE HARVEST OF TURTLE EGGS

A FRESH northeast breeze carried us full sail towards the Boca de la Tortuga. We landed at eleven in the morning on an island which the Indians of the missions of Uruana considered as their property, and which lies in the middle of the river. The island is celebrated for the turtle fishery, or, as they say here, "the harvest of eggs" that takes place annually.

We here found an assemblage of Indians encamped under huts made of palm leaves. This encampment contained more than three hundred persons. Accustomed since we had left San Fernando de Apure to see only deserted shores, we were singularly struck by the bustle that prevailed here. We found, besides the Guamos and the Ottomacs of Uruana, who are both considered savage races, Caribs and other Indians of the lower Orinoco. Every tribe was separately encamped, and was distinguished by the pigments with which their skins were painted. Some white men were seen amidst this tumultuous assemblage, chiefly *pulperos,* or small traders of Angostura, who had come up the river to purchase turtle oil from the natives.

The missionary of Uruana, a native of Alcala, came to meet us, and he was extremely astonished at seeing us. After having admired our instruments, he gave us an exaggerated picture of the sufferings to which we should be necessarily exposed in ascending the Orinoco beyond the cataracts. The object of our journey appeared to him very mysterious. "How is it possible to believe," said he, "that you have left your country to come and be devoured by mosquitoes on this river and to measure lands that are not your own?" . . .

We made the tour of the island, accompanied by the missionary and a pulpero who boasted of having for ten successive years visited the camp of the Indians and attended the turtle fishery. We were on a plain of sand perfectly smooth, and were told that, as far as we could see along the beach, turtle eggs were concealed under a layer of earth. . . .

The great turtle, or *arrau,* called by the Spaniards of the missions simply *tortuga,* is an animal whose existence is of great importance to the nations on the lower Orinoco. It is a large fresh-water tortoise. . . . The period at which the large tortoise lays its eggs coincides with the period of the lowest waters. . . . The lowest flats are found uncovered from the end of January till the 20th or 25th of March. The arrau tortoises collect in troops in the month of January, then issue from the water and warm themselves in the sun, reposing on the sands. The Indians believe that great heat is indispensable to the health of the animal and that its exposure to the sun favors the laying of the eggs. The arraus are found on the beach a great part of the day during the whole month of February. At the beginning of March the straggling troops assemble and swim toward the small number of islands on which they habitually deposit their eggs. It is probable that the same tortoise returns every year to the same locality. At this period, a few days before they lay their eggs, thousands of these animals may be seen ranged in long files on the borders of the islands . . . stretching out their necks and holding their heads above water to see whether they have anything to dread. The Indians, who are anxious that the bands when assembled should not separate, that the tortoises should not disperse, and that the laying of the eggs should be performed tranquilly, place sentinels at certain distances along the shore. The people who pass in boats are told to keep in the middle of the river and not frighten the tortoises by cries.

The laying of the eggs takes place always during the night, and it begins soon after sunset. With its hind feet, which are very long and furnished with crooked claws, the animal digs a hole three feet in diameter and two in depth. These tortoises feel so pressing a desire to lay their eggs that some of them descend into holes that have been dug by others but which are not yet covered with earth. There they deposit a new layer of eggs on that which has been recently laid. In this tumultuous movement an immense number of eggs are broken. . . . The number of animals working on the beach during the night is so considerable that day surprises many of them before the laying of their eggs is terminated. . . . The tortoises that thus remain too late are insensible to their own danger. They work in the presence of the Indians, who visit the beach at a very early hour, and who call them "mad tortoises." Notwithstanding the rapidity of their movements, they are then easily caught with the hand. . . .

When the camp is formed, the missionary of Uruana names his lieutenant, who divides the ground where the eggs are found into different portions, according to the number of the Indian tribes who take part in the gathering. . . .

THE TURTLES OF THE ORINOCO

The lieutenant begins his operations by sounding. He examines how far the stratum of eggs extends, by means of a long wooden or bamboo pole. This stratum, according to our measurements, extended to the distance of one hundred and twenty feet from the shore. Its average depth is three feet. The lieutenant places marks to indicate the point where each tribe should stop its labors.

We were surprised to hear this "harvest of eggs" estimated like the produce of a well-cultivated field. An area accurately measured of one hundred and twenty feet long and thirty feet wide has been known to yield one hundred jars of oil, valued at about forty pounds sterling. The Indians remove the earth with their hands; they place the eggs they have collected in small baskets, carry them to their encampment, and throw them into long wooden troughs filled with water. In these troughs the eggs, broken and stirred with shovels, remain exposed to the sun till the oily part, which floats on the surface, has time to thicken. As fast as this collects on the surface of the water, it is taken off and boiled over a quick fire. This animal oil, called *tortoise butter*, keeps the better, it is said, in proportion as it has undergone a strong boiling. When well prepared, it is limpid, odorless, and scarcely yellow. The missionaries compare it to the best olive oil, and it is used not merely for burning in lamps but for cooking.

A NARROW ESCAPE

OUR PILOT had anchored at the *Playa de Huevos* to purchase some provisions, our store having begun to run short. We found there fresh meat, Angostura rice, and even biscuit made of wheat flour. Our Indians filled the boat with little live turtles and eggs dried in the sun, for their own use. Having taken leave of the missionary of Uruana, who had treated us with great kindness, we set sail about four in the afternoon.

The wind was fresh and blew in squalls. Since we had entered the mountainous part of the country, we had discovered that our canoe carried sail very badly; but the master was desirous of showing the Indians who were assembled on the beach that, by going close to the wind, he could reach, at one single tack, the middle of the river. At the very moment when he was boasting of his dexterity and the boldness of his maneuver, the force of the wind upon the sail became so great that we were on the point of going down. One side of the boat was under water, which rushed in with such violence that it was soon up to our knees. It washed over a little table at which I was writing at the stern of the boat. I had some difficulty in saving my journal, and in an instant we saw our books, papers, and dried plants all afloat.

Bonpland was lying asleep in the middle of the canoe. Awakened by the entrance of the water and the cries of the Indians, he understood the danger of our situation, while he maintained that coolness which he always displayed in the most difficult circumstances. The lee side righting itself from time to time during the squall, he did not consider the boat as lost. He thought that, were we even forced to abandon it, we might save ourselves by swimming, since there was no crocodile in sight. Amidst this uncertainty the cordage of the sail suddenly gave way. The same gust of wind that had thrown us on our beam served also to right us. We labored to bale the water out of the boat with calabashes, the sail was again set, and in less than half an hour we were in a state to proceed. The wind now abated a little. Squalls alternating with dead calms are common in that part of the Orinoco which is bordered by mountains. They are very dangerous for boats deeply laden and without decks. We had escaped as if by a miracle. To the reproaches that were heaped on our pilot for having kept too near the wind, he replied with the phlegmatic coolness peculiar to the Indians, observing that the whites would find sun enough on those banks to dry their papers. . . .

UNDER THE MIDDAY SUN

WE LANDED in the middle of the strait of Baraguan to measure its breadth. . . . All the stones were covered with an innumerable quantity of iguanas and geckos [two kinds of lizards] with spreading and membranous fingers. These lizards, motionless with heads raised and mouths open, seemed to suck in the heated air. The thermometer placed against the rock rose to 122° F. The soil appeared to undulate from the effect of mirage, without a breath of wind being felt. The sun was near the zenith, and its dazzling light, reflected from the surface of the river, contrasted with the reddish vapors that enveloped every surrounding object.

How vivid is the impression produced by the calm of nature at noon in these burning climates! The beasts of the forests retire to the thickets; the birds hide themselves beneath the foliage of the trees or in the crevices of the rocks. Yet amidst this apparent silence, when we lend an attentive ear to the most feeble sounds transmitted through the air, we hear a dull vibration, a continual murmur, a hum of insects filling, if we may use the expression, all the lower strata of the air. Nothing is better fitted to make man feel the extent and power of organic life. Myriads of insects creep upon the soil and flutter round the plants parched by the heat of the sun.

A confused noise issues from every bush, from the decayed trunks of trees, from the clefts of the rocks, and from the ground undermined by lizards, millipedes, and *cecilias* [worm-like amphibians]. These are so many voices proclaiming to us that all nature breathes, and that, under a thousand different forms, life is diffused throughout the cracked and dusty soil as well as in the waters and in the air that circulates around us.

PAINTED INDIANS

THE INDIAN pilot, who had brought us from San Fernando de Apure as far as the shore of Pararuma, was unacquainted with the passage of the rapids of the Orinoco and would not undertake to conduct our bark any farther. We were obliged to conform to his will. Happily for us, the missionary of Carichana consented to sell us a fine canoe at a very moderate price. Father Bernardo Zea, missionary of the Atures and Maypures near the great cataracts, offered, though still unwell, to accompany us as far as the frontiers of Brazil. The number of natives who can assist in guiding boats through the *raudales* [rapids or cataracts] is so inconsiderable that, but for the presence of the monk, we should have risked spending whole weeks in these humid and unhealthy regions. . . .

Most of the missionaries of the upper and lower Orinoco permit the Indians of their missions to paint their skins. It is painful to add that some of them speculate on this barbarous practice of the natives. In their huts, pompously called "convents," I have often seen stores of *chica* [red pigment] which they sold as high as four francs a cake. To form a just idea of the extravagance of the decoration of these naked Indians, I must observe that with difficulty a man of large stature gains enough by the labor of a fortnight to procure in exchange the chica necessary to paint himself red. Thus, as we say in temperate climates of a poor man, "He has not enough to clothe himself," you hear the Indians of the Orinoco say, "That man is so poor that he has not enough to paint half his body." . . .

Does the use of *anato* [another red pigment] and chica derive its origin from the desire of pleasing and the taste for ornament so common among the most savage nations? Or must we suppose it to be founded on the observation that these coloring and oily matters with which the skin is plastered preserve it from the sting of the mosquitoes? I have often heard this question discussed in Europe; but in the missions of the Orinoco and wherever within the tropics the air is filled with venomous insects, the inquiry would appear absurd. The Carib and the Salive, who are painted red, are not less cruelly tormented by the mosquitoes and the gnats than the Indians whose bodies are plastered with no color. The sting of the insect causes no swelling in either, and scarcely ever produces those little pustules which occasion such smarting and itching to Europeans recently arrived. But the native and the white suffer equally from the sting till the insect has withdrawn its sucker from the skin. Bonpland and myself tried the expedient of rubbing our hands and arms with the fat of the crocodile and the oil of turtle eggs, but we never felt the least relief and were stung as before. . . .

The Indians are not always satisfied with one color uniformly spread. They sometimes imitate in the most whimsical manner, in painting their skin, the form of European garments. We saw some at Pararuma who were painted with blue jackets and black buttons. The missionaries related to us that the Guaynaves of the Río Caura are accustomed to stain them-

PAINTED INDIANS

selves red with anato, and to make broad transverse stripes on the body on which they stick spangles of silvery mica. Seen at a distance, these naked men appear to be dressed in lace clothes. If painted nations had been examined with the same attention as those who are clothed, it would have been perceived that the most fertile imagination and the most changeable caprice have created the fashions of painting as well as those of garments.

THEIR WRETCHED CANOE

THE NEW canoe intended for us was, like all Indian boats, a trunk of a tree hollowed out partly by the hatchet and partly by fire. It was forty feet long and three broad. Three persons could not sit in it side by side. These canoes are so cranky, and they require from their instability a cargo so equally distributed, that when you want to rise for an instant you must warn the rowers to lean to the opposite side. Without this precaution the water would necessarily enter the side pressed down. It is difficult to form an idea of the inconveniences that are suffered in such wretched vessels. . . .

We could not set sail before ten on the morning of the 10th. To gain something in breadth in our new canoe, a sort of latticework had been constructed on the stern with branches of trees that extended on each side beyond the gunwale. Unfortunately, the *toldo,* or roof of leaves, that covered this latticework was so low that we were obliged to lie down without seeing anything or, if seated, to sit nearly double. The necessity of carrying the canoe across the rapids and even from one river to another, and the fear of giving too much hold to the wind by making the toldo higher, render this construction necessary for vessels that go up towards the Río Negro.

CAMPING IN THE FOREST

The toldo was intended to cover four persons lying on the deck or latticework of brushwood, but our legs reached far beyond it, and when it rained, half our bodies were wet. Our couches consisted of ox hides or tiger skins spread upon branches of trees, which were painfully felt through so thin a covering. The fore part of the boat was filled with Indian rowers furnished with paddles three feet long, in the form of spoons. They were all naked, seated two by two, and they kept time in rowing with a surprising uniformity, singing songs of a sad and monotonous character.

The small cages containing our birds and monkeys, the number of which augmented as we advanced, were hung some to the toldo and others to the bow of the boat. This was our traveling menagerie. Notwithstanding the frequent losses occasioned by accidents and, above all, by the fatal effects of exposure to the sun, we had fourteen of these little animals alive at our return from the Casiquiare. . . . Every night, when we established our watch, our collection of animals and our instruments occupied the center. Around these were placed first our hammocks, then the hammocks of the Indians. On the outside were the fires which are thought indispensable against the attacks of the jaguar. About sunrise the monkeys in our cages answered the cries of the monkeys of the forest. These communications between animals of the same species sympathizing with one another, though unseen, one party enjoying that liberty which the other is deprived of, are somewhat melancholy and affecting.

In a canoe not three feet wide and so encumbered there remained no other place for the dried plants, trunks, a sextant, a dipping needle, and the meteorological instruments than the space below the latticework of branches, on which we were compelled to remain stretched the greater part of the day. If we wished to take the least object out of a trunk or to use an instrument, it was necessary to row ashore and land. To these inconveniences were joined the torment of the mosquitoes which swarmed under the toldo and the heat radiated from the leaves of the palm trees, whose upper surface was continually exposed to the sun's rays. We attempted to mend our situation every instant, but always without success. While one of us hid himself under a sheet to ward off the insects, the other insisted on having green wood lighted beneath the toldo in the hope of driving away the mosquitoes by the smoke. The painful sensations of the eyes and the increase of heat, already stifling, rendered both these contrivances alike impracticable. With some gaiety of temper, with feelings of mutual good will, and with a vivid taste for the majestic grandeur of these vast valleys of rivers, travelers easily support evils that become habitual.

In the next section Humboldt gives a glimpse of the geological and biological past of South America. He recognized the vast changes that had taken place in the earth's surface and in the animal and plant life that inhabited it. Charles Darwin read Humboldt's account and saw the same things in South America some thirty years later. What Humboldt saw and marveled at, Darwin later explained in his theory of evolution.

GLIMPSES OF PAST AGES

THE ORINOCO was already three feet higher than the level of the lowest waters. The natives showed us on a granite wall the traces of the great rise of the waters of late years. We found them to be forty-two feet high, which is double the mean rise of the Nile. . . . It is an unquestionable fact that Carichana, at San Borja, at Atures, and at Maypures, wherever the river has forced its way through the mountains, you see at a hundred, sometimes at a hundred and thirty feet above the highest present swell of the river, black bands and erosions that indicate the ancient levels of the waters. Is this river, then, which appears to us so grand and so majestic, only the feeble remains of those immense currents of fresh water which heretofore traversed the country east of the Andes, like arms of inland seas? What must have been the state of those low countries of Guiana that now undergo the effects of annual inundations? What immense numbers of crocodiles, manatees, and boas must have inhabited these vast spaces of land converted al-

ternately into marshes of stagnant water and into barren and
fissured plains! The more peaceful world which we inhabit
has, then, succeeded a world of tumult.

The bones of mastodons and American elephants are found
dispersed on the tablelands of the Andes. The *Megatherium*
[giant ground sloth] inhabited the plains of Uruguay. On
digging deep into the ground in high valleys where neither
palm trees nor tree-like ferns can grow, strata of coal are discovered that still show vestiges of gigantic monocotyledonous
plants [such as grasses and palms]. There was a remote period,
then, in which the classes of plants were otherwise distributed,
when the animals were larger and the rivers broader and of
greater depth. There end those records of nature that it is in
our power to consult.

THE GREAT CATARACTS

IN ASCENDING the Orinoco more to the south, the heat, far
from increasing, became more bearable. . . . The torment of
the mosquitoes augmented severely, notwithstanding the de-
crease of heat. We never suffered so much from them as at San
Borja. We could neither speak nor uncover our faces without
having our mouths and noses filled with insects. We were surprised not to find the thermometer at 95° or 96° F.; the extreme irritation of the skin made us believe that the air was
scorching. We passed the night on the beach of Guaripo. The
fear of the little caribe fish prevented us from bathing. The
crocodiles we had met with this day were of an extraordinary
size, from twenty-two to twenty-four feet.

Our sufferings from the gnats made us depart at five o'clock
on the morning of the 14th. . . . The mountains of the Great

Cataracts bounded the horizon towards the southeast. In proportion as we advanced, the shores of the Orinoco exhibited a more imposing and picturesque aspect.

The river of the Orinoco, in running from south to north, is crossed by a chain of granitic mountains. Twice confined in its course, it turbulently breaks on the rocks that form steps and transverse dikes. Nothing can be grander than the aspect of this spot. Neither the fall of the Tequendama, near Santa Fé de Bogotá, nor the magnificent scenes of the Cordilleras could weaken the impression produced upon my mind by the first view of the rapids of Atures and of Maypures. When the spectator is so stationed that the eye can at once take in the long succession of cataracts, the immense sheet of foam and vapors illumined by the rays of the setting sun, the whole river seems as if it were suspended over its bed. . . .

We did not arrive till very late at the foot of the Great Cataract in a bay called the *lower harbor*. We followed, not without difficulty in a dark night, the narrow path that leads to the mission of Atures, three miles distant from the river. We crossed a plain covered with large blocks of granite. . . .

When the dikes, or natural dams, are only two or three feet high, the Indians venture to descend them in boats. In going up the river they swim on ahead, and if after many vain efforts they succeed in fixing a rope to one of the points of rock that crown the dike, by means of that rope they then draw the bark to the top of the rapid. The boat, during this arduous task, often fills with water; at other times it is stove against the rocks, and the Indians, their bodies bruised and bleeding, extricate themselves with difficulty from the whirlpools and by swimming reach the nearest island. When the steps or rocky

AT THE CATARACTS

barriers are very high and entirely bar the river, light boats are carried on shore, and with the help of branches of trees placed under them to serve as rollers, they are drawn as far as the place where the river again becomes navigable. This operation is seldom necessary when the water is high. . . .

On the 16th of April, towards evening, we received tidings that in less than six hours our boat had passed the rapids and had arrived in good condition in a cover called the *Port of the Expedition.* . . .

After having spent two days near the cataract of Atures, we were not sorry when our boat was reladen. . . . We were horribly tormented in the day by mosquitoes and the *jejen,* a small venomous fly, and at night by the *zancudos,* a large species of gnat dreaded even by the natives. Our hands began to swell considerably, and this swelling increased daily till

our arrival on the banks of the Temi. The means that are
employed to escape from these little plagues are very extraordinary. The good missionary Bernardo Zea, who passed his
life tormented by mosquitoes, had constructed near the church
[at Atures], on a scaffolding of trunks of palm trees, a small
apartment in which we breathed more freely. To this we went
up in the evenings, by means of a ladder, to dry our plants
and write our journal. The missionary had justly observed
that the insects abounded more particularly in the lowest
strata of the atmosphere, that which reaches from the ground
to the height of twelve or fifteen feet. . . .

It is neither the dangers of navigating in small boats, the
savage Indians, nor the serpents, crocodiles, or jaguars that
make Spaniards dread a voyage on the Orinoco. It is, they say
with simplicity, "el sudar y las moscos" (the perspiration and
the flies). . . .

We have just seen that winged insects collected in society
and concealing in their sucker a liquid that irritates the skin
are capable of rendering vast countries almost uninhabitable.
In several hot and temperate parts of the equinoctial zone,
other insects equally small—the termites—create obstacles to
the progress of civilization that are difficult to be surmounted.
They devour paper, pasteboard, and parchment with frightful
rapidity, utterly destroying records and libraries. Whole provinces of Spanish America do not possess one written docu-
ment that dates a hundred years back.

*On the morning of April 17, Humboldt and Bonpland
set out again in their canoe, headed towards the cataracts
of Maypures. The Indians hauled the craft successfully*

over the rapids, and after narrowly escaping being swept back down again by the swift current, they arrived safely at the little village of Maypures on the banks of the upper cataract. Two days later they set out once more in the same canoe, now much damaged by its trip through the rapids. The traveler "feels as if he were in a new world," Humboldt reported, when he had passed the Great Cataracts and had crossed the barrier between the civilized coastal lands and the savage and unknown interior.

A few nights later they left the Orinoco and at sunrise found themselves in new surroundings on the Atabapo River. This river would take them, by the portage of Pimichin, to the Río Negro on the frontier of Brazil.

CHAPTER SIX

A CIRCLE OF RIVERS

UP THE ATABAPO

EVERYTHING CHANGES on entering the Río Atabapo: the constitution of the atmosphere, the color of the waters, and the form of the trees that cover the shore. You no longer suffer during the day the torment of mosquitoes, and the long-legged gnats become rare during the night. Beyond the mission of San Fernando de Atabapo these nocturnal insects disappear altogether. The water of the Orinoco is turbid and loaded with earthy matter; and in the coves, from the accumulation of dead crocodiles and other putrescent substances, it diffused a musky and faint smell. We were sometimes obliged to strain this water through a linen cloth before we drank it. The water of the Atabapo, on the contrary, is pure, agreeable to the taste, and without any trace of smell. . . .

The extreme purity of the black waters is proved by their limpidity, their transparency, and the clearness with which they reflect the images and colors of surrounding objects. The smallest fish are visible in them at a depth of twenty or thirty feet; and most commonly the bottom of the river may be distinguished, which is . . . a quartzose and granitic sand of dazzling whiteness. . . .

The river Atabapo presents throughout a peculiar aspect; you see nothing of its real banks, formed by flat lands eight or ten feet high; they are concealed by a row of palms and small trees with slender trunks whose roots are bathed by the waters. . . . Enormous water snakes, resembling the boa in shape, are unfortunately very common and are dangerous to Indians who bathe. We saw them almost from the first day we embarked, swimming by the side of our canoe. They were at most twelve or fourteen feet long. The jaguars of the banks of the Atabapo and the Temi are large and well fed. They are said, however, to be less daring than the jaguars of the Orinoco. . . .

On the 29th the air was cooler. . . . We still advanced but slowly from the force of the current, and we stopped a great part of the day to seek for plants. It was night when we arrived at the mission of San Balthasar. . . .

The night of the 30th of April was sufficiently fine for observing the meridian heights of alpha [star] of the Southern Cross and the two large stars in the feet of the Centaur. I found the latitude of San Balthasar to be 3° 14′ 21″. Hourly angles of the sun gave 70° 14′ 21″ for the longitude by the chronometer. . . .

The canoe carrying Humboldt and Bonpland left the Atabapo and entered the Temi River. The bends and turns of this river flooded the forest around it, and so, to shorten the route, the Indian piloting the canoe left the bed of the river and went through the woods along paths that were now under water. An Indian with a large knife stood at the head of the boat, chopping down branches that obstructed the passage.

The Temi River took them to another little river, the Tuamini, and they proceeded along this to the mission of

Javita. At this small settlement they found the help they needed to transport their canoe overland (portage) to the Río Negro.

THE PORTAGE

WE WENT every day to see how our canoe advanced on the portages. Twenty-three Indians were employed in dragging it by land, placing branches of trees to serve as rollers. In this manner a small boat proceeds in a day or a day and a half from the waters of the Tuamini to those of the Caño Pimichin, which flow into the Río Negro. Our canoe being very large and having to pass the cataracts a second time, it was necessary to avoid any friction on the bottom with particular care. Consequently, the passage occupied more than four days. It is only since 1795 that a road has been traced through the forest. By substituting a canal for this portage, as I proposed to the ministry of King Charles IV, the communication between the Río Negro and Angostura, between the Spanish Orinoco and the Portuguese possessions on the Amazon, would be singularly facilitated. . . .

Four days had passed and our canoe had not yet arrived at the landing place of the Río Pimichin. "You want for nothing in my mission," said Father Cereso. "You have plaintains and fish; at night you are not stung by mosquitoes; and the longer you stay, the better chance you will have of seeing the stars of my country. If your boat be destroyed in the portage, we will give you another. . . ." Notwithstanding our impatience, we listened with interest to the information given us by the worthy missionary. It confirmed all we had already heard of the moral state of the natives of those countries. They live, distributed in hordes of forty or fifty, under a family government, and they recognize a common chief only at times when they make war against their neighbors. The mistrust of these hordes towards one another is increased by the circumstance that those who live in the nearest neighborhood speak languages altogether different. . . . In open countries, or in a state of advanced civilization, communication by rivers contributes powerfully to generalize languages, manners, and political institutions. But in the impenetrable forests of the torrid zone, as in the first rude condition of our species, rivers increase the dismemberment of great nations, favor the transition of dialects into languages that appear to us radically distinct, and keep up national hatred and mistrust. . . . Men avoid, because they do not understand, each other; they mutually hate, because they mutually fear. . . .

The nations of the upper Orinoco, the Atabapo, and the Inirida, like the ancient Germans and the Persians, have no other worship than that of the powers of nature. They call the good principle *Cachimana;* it is the *Manitou,* the Great Spirit, that regulates the seasons and favors the harvests. Along with Cachimana there is an evil principle, *Iolokiamo,* less powerful but more artful and, in particular, more active. The Indians of the forest, when they occasionally visit the missions, conceive with difficulty the idea of a temple or an image. "These good people," said the missionary, "like only processions in the open air. When I last celebrated the festival of San Antonio, the patron of my village, the Indians of Inirida were present at mass. 'Your God,' said they to me, 'keeps himself shut up in a house, as if he were old and infirm; ours is in the forest, in the fields, and on the mountains of Sipapu, whence the rains come.' "

On the 5th of May we set off to follow our canoe on foot. It had at length arrived by the portage at the Caño Pimichin. We had to ford a great number of streams; and these passages require some caution on account of the vipers with which the marshes abound. . . .

The travelers now had to make a decision. They could go on down the Río Negro to the Amazon and out to the Atlantic Ocean by that great river. Or they could go only as far as the Casiquiare, through it to the Orinoco, and back up to the northeast coast of Venezuela. Either route would take them from twenty to thirty days.

The trip down the Amazon must have been a tempting prospect, for no man had ever traversed this vast and disputed system of inland waterways. But in San Carlos, near the Brazilian border and just beyond the junction of the Casiquiare, they were told that for political reasons they might encounter difficulties in passing from Spanish territory to the Portuguese colony of Brazil. This decided them. They would follow the Casiquiare back to the Orinoco.

It was a fortunate decision. After his return to Europe, Humboldt learned that the governor of the Brazilian province into which he would have ventured had orders to arrest and imprison him. Nearly a half-century later Humboldt saw a copy of the warrant ordering his arrest. It was dated June 2, 1800. The Portuguese officials feared that his scientific observations were merely a pretext which "might possibly conceal plans for the spread of new ideas and dangerous principles among the faithful subjects of this realm at a time when the temper of the nation is in a condition so dangerous and so difficult to deal with."

BEGINNING THE RETURN TRIP

ON THE 10th of May, our canoe being ready before sunrise, we embarked to go up the Río Negro as far as the mouth of the Casiquiare, and to devote ourselves to researches on the real course of that river which unites the Orinoco to the Amazon. The morning was fine, but in proportion as the heat augmented, the sky became obscured. . . . We were more grieved every day at the aspect of the cloudy sky. Bonpland was losing by this excessive humidity the plants he had collected; and I, for my part, was afraid lest I should again find the fogs of the Río Negro in the valley of the Casiquiare.

No one in these missions for half a century had doubted the existence of communication between two great systems of rivers. The important point of our voyage was confined, therefore, to fixing by astronomical observations the course of the Casiquiare and particularly the point of its entrance into the Río Negro and that of the bifurcation of the Orinoco. Without a sight of the sun and the stars, this object would be frustrated and we should have exposed ourselves in vain to long and painful privations. Our fellow travelers would have returned by the shortest way, that of the Pimichin and the small rivers; but Bonpland preferred, like me, persisting in the plan of the voyage which we had traced for ourselves in passing the Great Cataracts. We had already traveled five hundred and forty miles in a boat from San Fernando de Apure to San Carlos, on the Río Apure, the Orinoco, the Atabapo, the Temi, the Tuamini, and the Río Negro. In again entering the Orinoco by the Casiquiare we had to navigate nine hundred and sixty miles from San Carlos to Angostura. By this way we had to struggle against the currents during ten days; the rest was to be performed by going down the stream of the Orinoco. We would have been to blame if we had suffered ourselves to be discouraged by the fear of a cloudy sky and by the mosquitoes of the Casiquiare. Our Indian pilot, who had recently been at Mandavaca, promised us the sun and "those great stars that eat the clouds" as soon as we should have left the "black waters." We therefore carried out our first project of returning to San Fernando de Atabapo by the Casiquiare. Fortunately for our researches, the prediction of the Indian was verified. The "white waters" brought us by degrees a more serene sky, stars, mosquitoes, and crocodiles.

A TRAVELING MENAGERIE

In one of the huts of the Pacimonales [Indians] we purchased two fine large birds, a toucan and a species of macaw, seventeen inches long, having the whole body of a purple color. We had already in our canoe seven parrots, two manakins [kind of small bird], a motmot [a jay-like bird], two guans [jungle fowl], two manaviris [weasel cats], and eight monkeys [of five different species, three of which were new].

Father Zea whispered some complaints at the daily augmentation of this ambulatory collection. The toucan resembles the raven in manners and intelligence. It is a courageous animal, but easily tamed. Its long and stout beak serves to defend it at a distance. It makes itself master of the house, steals whatever it can come at, and loves to bathe often and fish on the banks of the river. The toucan we had bought was very young; yet it took delight, during the whole voyage, in teasing

TRAVELING MENAGERIE

the nocturnal monkeys, which are melancholy and irritable. . . .

Most of our animals were confined in small wicker cages; others ran at full liberty in all parts of the boat. At the approach of rain the macaws sent forth noisy cries, the toucan wanted to reach the shore to fish, and the little monkeys (the titis) went in search of Father Zea, to take shelter in the large sleeves of his Franciscan habit. These incidents sometimes amused us so much that we forgot the torment of the mosquitoes.

CANNIBALISM

WE FOUND at Mandavaca the good old missionary who had already spent "twenty years of mosquitoes in the bosques del Casiquiare," and whose legs were so spotted by the stings of insects that the color of the skin could scarcely be perceived. He talked to us of his solitude and of the sad necessity which often compelled him to leave the most atrocious crimes unpunished in the two missions of Mandavaca and Vasiva. In the latter place an Indian alcalde had a few years before eaten one of his wives, after having taken her to his *conuco* [a hut outside the missions] and fattened her for good feeding.

The cannibalism of the nations of Venezuela is never caused by want of subsistence or by the superstitions of their religion, as in the islands of the South Sea, but is generally the effect of the vengeance of a conqueror and (as the missionaries say) "of a vitiated appetite." Victory over a hostile tribe is celebrated by a repast in which some parts of the body of a prisoner are devoured. Sometimes a defenseless family is surprised in the night, or an enemy who is met with by chance in the woods is killed by a poisoned arrow. The body is cut to pieces and carried as a trophy to the hut.

It is civilization only that has made man feel the unity of the human race—which has revealed to him, as we may say, the ties of consanguinity by which he is linked to beings to whose language and manners he is a stranger. Savages know only their own family, and a tribe appears to them but a more numerous assemblage of relations. When those who inhabit the missions see Indians of the forest who are unknown to them arrive, they make use of an expression which has struck us by its simple candor: "They are, no doubt, my relations; I understand them when they speak to me." But these very savages detest all who are not of their family or their tribe, and hunt the Indians of a neighboring tribe, who live at war with their own, as we hunt game. They know the duties of family ties and of relationship, but not those of humanity, which require the feeling of a common tie with beings framed like ourselves. No emotion of pity prompts them to spare the wives or children of a hostile race, and the latter are devoured in preference at the repast given at the conclusion of a battle or warlike incursion. . . .

Reproaches addressed to the natives on the abominable practice which we here discuss produce no effect; it is as if a Brahmin, traveling in Europe, were to reproach us with the habit of feeding on the flesh of animals. . . .

> *From the 14th to the 21st of May they paddled through an extremely wild and unfrequented region of the Casiquiare. Most of the time there were no banks on which they could land, but simply great walls of trees covered with vines that hung down to the water. The last night before reaching the Orinoco they slept in a forest of palm trees, and, although it rained violently, the foliage over them was so dense that they were perfectly sheltered. Their fires "lit up, to the height of fifty or sixty feet, the palm trees, the lianas loaded with flowers, and the columns of white smoke which ascended in a straight line towards the sky. The whole exhibited a magnificent spectacle."*
>
> *On May 21 they reached Esmeralda on the Orinoco.*

PREPARING CURARE AT ESMERALDA

ESMERALDA IS the most celebrated spot on the Orinoco for the preparation of that active poison [*curare*] which is employed in war, in the chase, and, singularly enough, as a remedy for gastric derangements. . . .

When we arrived at Esmeralda, the greater part of the

Indians were returning from an excursion which they had
made to the east, beyond the Río Padamo, to gather *juvias*
[Brazil nuts] and the liana which yields the curare. Their return was celebrated by a festival which is called in the mission
"la fiesta de las juvias," and which resembles our "harvest
homes" and vintage feasts. The women had prepared a
quantity of fermented liquor, and during two days the Indians
were in a state of intoxication. Among nations who attach
great importance to the fruit of the palm and of some other
trees useful for the nourishment of man, the period when
these fruits are gathered is marked by public rejoicings, and
time is divided according to these festivals, which succeed
one another in an invariably regular course.

We were fortunate enough to find an old Indian more temperate than the rest, who was employed in preparing the
curare poison from freshly gathered plants. He was the chemist of the place. We found at his dwelling large earthen pots
for boiling the vegetable juice, shallower vessels to favor the
evaporation by a larger surface, and leaves of the plantain
tree rolled up in the shape of our filters and used to filtrate
the liquids, more or less loaded with fibrous matter. The
greatest order and neatness prevailed in this hut, which was
transformed into a chemical laboratory. The old Indian was
known throughout the mission by the name of the poison master (*amo del curare*). He had that self-sufficient air and tone
of pedantry of which the pharmacologists of Europe were
formerly accused. "I know," said he, "that the whites have the
secret of making soap and manufacturing that black powder
which has the defect of making a noise when used in killing
animals. The curare which we prepare from father to son is
superior to anything you can make 'down yonder.' It is the

juice of an herb which kills silently, without anyone knowing whence the stroke comes."

This chemical operation, to which the old man attached so much importance, appeared to us extremely simple. The *bejuco* (liana) used at Esmeralda for the preparation of the poison . . . is the *bejuco de mavacure,* which is gathered in abundance east of the mission on the left bank of the Orinoco. . . . A cold infusion is first prepared by pouring water on the fibrous matter which is the ground bark of the mavacure. A yellowish water filters during several hours, drop by drop, through the leafy funnel. This filtered water is the poisonous liquor, but it acquires strength only when concentrated by evaporation, like molasses, in a large earthen pot. The Indian from time to time invited us to taste the liquid; its taste, more or less bitter, decides when the concentration by fire has been carried sufficiently far. There is no danger in tasting it, the curare being poisonous only when it comes into immediate contact with the blood. . . .

The curare is sold in little calabashes; but, its preparation being in the hands of a few families, and the quantity of poison attached to each dart being extremely small, the best curare, that of Esmeralda and Mandavaca, is sold at a very high price. This substance, when dried, resembles opium; but it strongly absorbs moisture when exposed to the air. Its taste is an agreeable bitter, and Bonpland and myself have often swallowed small portions of it. There is no danger in so doing if it be certain that neither lips nor gums bleed. . . . Scarcely a fowl is eaten on the banks of the Orinoco which has not been killed with a poisoned arrow; and the missionaries allege that the flesh of animals is never so good as when this method is employed. . . . Travelers, on arriving in the missions, fre-

PREPARING CURARE

quently testify their apprehension on learning that the fowls,
monkeys, guanas, and even the fish which they eat have been
killed with poisoned arrows. But these fears are groundless.
. . . The danger of the curare results only from the action of
the poison on the circulatory system.

The opinion is very general in the missions that no cure is
possible if the curare is fresh, well concentrated, and has
stayed long enough in the wound to have entered freely
into the circulation. . . . Indians who had been wounded in
battle by weapons dipped in the curare described to us the
symptoms they experienced, which were entirely similar to
those observed in the bite of serpents. The wounded person
feels congestion in the head, vertigo, and nausea. He is tor-

mented by a raging thirst, and numbness pervades all the parts that are near the wound.

FESTIVAL OF THE BRAZIL NUTS

THE OLD Indian seemed flattered by the interest we took in his chemical processes. He found us sufficiently intelligent to lead him to the belief that we knew how to make soap, an art which, next to the preparation of curare, appeared to him one of the finest of human inventions. When the liquid poison had been poured into the vessels prepared for their reception, we accompanied the Indian to the "festival of the juvias."

The harvest of juvias was celebrated by dancing and by excesses of wild intoxication. The hut where the natives were assembled displayed during several days a very singular aspect. There was neither table nor bench; but large roasted monkeys, blackened by smoke, were ranged in regular order against the wall. These were the *marimondes* [spider monkeys] and those bearded monkeys called *capuchins*. . . .

We saw the Indians dance. The monotony of their dancing is increased by the women not daring to take part in it. The men, young and old, form a circle, holding each other's hands, and turn sometimes to the right, sometimes to the left, for whole hours with silent gravity. Most frequently the dancers themselves are the musicians. Feeble sounds, drawn from a series of reeds of different lengths, form a slow and plaintive accompaniment. . . .

At the festival of which we were spectators, the women, who were excluded from the dance and every sort of public rejoicing, were daily occupied in serving the men with roasted mon-

key, fermented liquors, and palm cabbage. This last production has the taste of our cauliflowers, and in no other country
had we seen specimens of such an immense size. . . . Another
substance, which is much more nutritive, is obtained from
the animal kingdom. This is "fish flour." The Indians
throughout the upper Orinoco fry fish, dry them in the sun,
and reduce them to powder without separating the bones. I
have seen masses of fifty or sixty pounds of this flour, which
resembles that of cassava. When it is wanted for eating, it is
mixed with water and reduced to a paste. . . .

At Esmeralda, as everywhere else throughout the missions,
the Indians who will not be baptized and who are merely ag-
gregated in the community live in a state of polygamy. The
number of wives differs much in different tribes. It is most
considerable among the Caribs and all the nations that have
preserved the custom of carrying off young girls from the
neighboring tribes. How can we imagine domestic happiness
in so unequal an association? The women live in a sort of
slavery, as they do in most nations which are in a state of
barbarism. . . .

When an Indian who lives in polygamy becomes a Christian, he is compelled by the missionaries to choose among his
wives the one he prefers and to reject the others. At the
moment of separation the new convert sometimes discovers the
most valuable qualities in the wives he is obliged to abandon.
One understands gardening perfectly; another knows how to
prepare *chiza,* an intoxicating beverage extracted from the
root of cassava; all appear to him alike clever and useful. Sometimes the desire of preserving his wives overcomes in the
Indian his inclination to Christianity. But most frequently,

in his perplexity, the husband prefers submitting to the choice
of the missionary as to a blind fatality.

THREE MORE WEEKS BY CANOE

WE LEFT the mission of Esmeralda on the 23rd of May. Without being positively ill, we felt ourselves in a state of languor
and weakness, caused by the torment of insects, bad food, and
a long voyage in narrow and damp boats. . . . Our canoe was
not ready to receive us till near three o'clock in the afternoon.
It had been filled with innumerable swarms of ants during the
navigation of the Casiquiare; and the toldo, or roof of palm
leaves, beneath which we were again doomed to remain
stretched out during twenty-two days, was with difficulty
cleared of these insects. . . .

From the 24th to the 27th of May we slept but twice on
land. The Orinoco being free from shoals, the Indian pilot
pursued his course all night, abandoning the boat to the current of the river. Setting apart the time which we spent on the
shore in preparing the rice and plantains that served us for
food, we took but thirty-five hours in going from Esmeralda
to Santa Barbara. . . .

The mission of Santa Barbara is situated a little to the west
of the mouth of the Río Ventuari. We found in this small
village of one hundred and twenty inhabitants some traces of
industry, but the produce of this industry is of little profit to
the natives. It is reserved for the monks, or, as they say in
these countries, for the church and the convent. We were assured that a great lamp of massive silver, purchased at the
expense of the neophytes, is expected from Madrid. Let us
hope that after the arrival of this treasure they will think also

of clothing the Indians, of procuring for them some instruments of agriculture, and assembling their children in a school. Although there are a few oxen in the savannas round the mission, they are rarely employed in turning the mill to press out the juice of the sugar cane. This is the occupation of the Indians, who work without pay here as they do everywhere when they are understood to work for the church. . . .

On the 27th of May we arrived at San Fernando de Atabapo. We lodged in the same house which we had occupied a month previously when going up the Río Negro. We then directed our course towards the south, by the Atabapo and the Temi. We were now returning from the west, having made a long circuit by the Casiquiare and the upper Orinoco.

We remained only one day at San Fernando de Atabapo, although that village, adorned as it was by the pirijao palm tree, with fruit like peaches, appeared to us a delicious abode. . . .

We recalled to mind with much satisfaction the scenes where we had reposed in going up the river. We again found the Indians who had accompanied us in our botanizing. . . . From the mouth of the Atabapo as far as that of the Apure we seemed to be traveling as through a country which we had long inhabited. We were reduced to the same abstinence; we were stung by the same mosquitoes; but the certainty of reaching in a few weeks the term of our physical sufferings kept up our spirits.

THE LONG JOURNEY'S END

IT WOULD be difficult for me to express the satisfaction we felt on landing at Angostura [Bolívar], the capital of Spanish

Guiana [now part of Venezuela]. The inconveniences endured at sea in small vessels are trivial in comparison with those that are suffered under a burning sky, surrounded by swarms of mosquitoes and lying stretched in a canoe without the possibility of taking the least bodily exercise.

In seventy-five days we had performed a passage of fifteen hundred miles on the five great rivers Apure, Orinoco, Atabapo, Negro, and Casiquiare, and in this vast extent we had found but a very small number of inhabited places. After the life we had led in the woods, our dress was not in the very best order, yet nevertheless Bonpland and I hastened to present ourselves to Don Felipe de Ynciarte, the governor of the province of Guiana. He received us in the most cordial manner and lodged us in the house of the secretary of the Intendencia. Coming from an almost deserted country, we were struck with the bustle of the town, though it contained only six thousand inhabitants. We admired the conveniences which industry and commerce furnish to civilized man. Humble dwellings appeared to us magnificent, and every person with whom we conversed seemed to be endowed with superior intelligence. Long privations give a value to the smallest enjoyments, and I cannot express the pleasure we felt when we first saw wheat bread on the governor's table. Sensations of this sort are doubtless familiar to all who have made distant voyages.

A painful circumstance obliged us to sojourn a whole month in the town of Angostura. We felt ourselves on the first days after our arrival tired and enfeebled, but in perfect health. Monsieur Bonpland began to examine the small number of plants which he had been able to save from the influence of the damp climate, and I was occupied in settling by astronomical observations the longitude and latitude of the capital, as well as the dip of the magnetic needle.

These labors were soon interrupted. We were both attacked almost on the same day by a disorder which with my fellow traveler took the character of a debilitating fever. At this period the air was most healthful at Angostura, and as the only mulatto servant we had brought from Cumaná felt symptoms of the same disorder, it was suspected that we had imbibed the germs of typhus in the damp forests of the Casiquiare. It is common enough for travelers to feel no effects from miasmata [polluted air] till, on arriving in a purer atmosphere, they begin to enjoy repose. . . . The fever was continual, and, as almost always happens in the tropics, it was accompanied by dysentery. Bonpland displayed that courage and mildness of character which never forsook him in the most trying situations. I was agitated by sad presages, for I remembered that the botanist Loefling, a pupil of Linnaeus, died not far from Angostura, a victim of his zeal for the progress of natural history. We had not yet passed a year in the torrid zone, and my too faithful memory conjured up everything I had read in Europe on the dangers of the atmosphere inhaled in the forests. Instead of going up the Orinoco we might have sojourned some months in the temperate and healthful climate of the Sierra Nevada de Merida. It was I who had chosen the path of the rivers, and the danger of my fellow traveler presented itself to my mind as the fatal consequence of this imprudent choice.

After having attained in a few days an extraordinary degree of violence, the fever assumed a less alarming character. . . . The recovery of the patient, however, was extremely slow, as always happens with Europeans who are not thoroughly seasoned to the climate. The period of the rains drew near, and in order to return to the coast of Cumaná it was necessary again to cross the llanos, where, amidst half-inundated lands, it is rare to find shelter or any other food than meat dried in the sun. To avoid exposing Bonpland to a dangerous relapse, we resolved to stay at Angostura till the 10th of July. We spent part of this time at a neighboring plantation where mango trees and breadfruit trees were cultivated. The latter had attained in the tenth year a height of more than forty feet.

CHAPTER SEVEN

A SIDE TRIP TO CUBA

As soon as Bonpland recovered, he and Humboldt started back to Cumaná. They reached there September 1, 1800, a little more than a year after their arrival from Europe. In spite of all the hardships of the journey, they had mapped a vast unknown area of South America and had collected thousands of species of plants—more than any exploring botanists ever had before. In a letter to a botanist friend Humboldt wrote:

What an infinite store of plants are treasured up in that wonderful tract of country lying between the Orinoco and the Amazon, through which I have traveled 6,443 miles in a district abounding with impenetrable forests and peopled with apes of species hitherto unknown! We were scarcely able to collect a tenth of the plants we met with. I am now perfectly convinced of a fact concerning which I was exceedingly incredulous when I was in England . . . that we are not as yet acquainted with three fifths of all the existing plants on earth!

Humboldt felt completely happy and at home on this return visit to Cumaná. He wrote his brother, Wilhelm, at this time that he could not possibly have been placed in circumstances more favorable for study and investigation. He was "free from the manifold distractions constantly arising in civilized life from the claims of society."

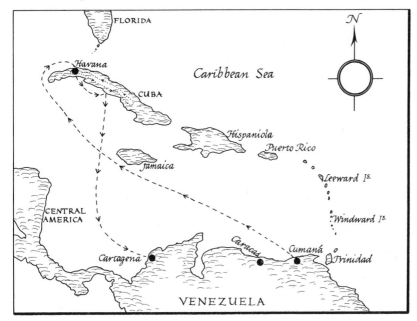

To Cuba and Back

The only drawbacks to this solitude, he said, were the want of information as to the progress science was making in Europe, and the lack of the give-and-take of discussion with other scientists.

Late in November, Humboldt and Bonpland sailed for Cuba in a small vessel loaded with salted meat. Humboldt wanted to study Cuba because of its political importance in the Americas. It had great possibilities, he thought, because of its large area, its fertile soil, its naval establishments, and because three fifths of its population consisted of free men.

After a twenty-five-day sail in constant bad weather Humboldt and Bonpland were happy to see the gay and picturesque port of Havana. "But alas!" Humboldt wrote, "we grieve almost to tears when we open our cases

*of plants! . . . The extreme humidity of the South Ameri-
can climate has caused more than one third of our collection to be destroyed. We are daily discovering new insects
destructive to paper and plants. Camphor, turpentine,
tar, pitched boards, and other preservatives successful in
a European climate prove quite useless here. . . ."*

*Humboldt devoted a great deal of time, with little
sleep, to the study of the land and the people of this important island. The result, years later, was a long* Political
Essay on the Island of Cuba. *The distinguishing feature
of this study is Humboldt's passionate and powerful de-
nunciation of slavery. In Europe he had hated the idea of
slavery. In Venezuela and Cuba he saw the reality and
determined to do everything in his power to eliminate
this evil from the earth.*

*More than fifty years later, while the Fugitive Slave
Law was in force in the United States, he succeeded in
persuading the Prussian government to enact a law that
freed every slave who touched its soil. The very same year,
1856, he threw the weight of his great reputation behind
Colonel Frémont, the Presidential candidate whom the
abolitionists in America supported against James Bu-
chanan. Humboldt had always feared that slavery in the
United States was a threat to the continued existence of
the Union. Less than two years after his death the American Civil War began.*

REFLECTIONS ON SLAVERY

It is for the traveler who has been an eyewitness of the suffering and the degradation of human nature to make the complaints of the unfortunate reach the ear of those by whom they

can be relieved. I observed the condition of the blacks in
countries where the laws, the religion, and the national habits
tend to mitigate their fate. Yet I retained, on quitting America,
the same horror of slavery which I had felt in Europe. . . .

Slavery is no doubt the greatest evil that afflicts human
nature, whether we consider the slave torn from his family in
his native country and thrown into the hold of a slave ship, or
as making part of a flock of black men parked on the soil of
the West Indies. But for individuals there are degrees of suffering and privation. How great is the difference in the condition of the slave who serves in the house of a rich family at
Havana or at Kingston, or one who works for himself, giving
his master but a daily retribution [compensation], and that of
a slave attached to a sugar estate! The threats employed to
correct an obstinate Negro mark this scale of human privations. The coachman is menaced with the coffee plantation,
and the slave working on the latter is menaced with the sugar
house.

The Negro who with his wife inhabits a separate hut, whose
heart is warmed by those feelings of affection which for the
most part characterize the African race, finds that after his
labor some care is taken of him amidst his indigent family, is
in a position not to be compared with that of the insulated
slave lost in the mass. This diversity of condition escapes the
notice of those who have not had the spectacle of the West
Indies before their eyes. . . . The luxury of the masters and the
possibility of gain by their work have drawn more than eighty
thousand slaves to the towns; and the manumission of them,
favored by the wisdom of the laws, is become so active as to
have produced at the present period more than 130,000 free
men of color. . . .

The impulse may be given by these European governments which have a right comprehension of human dignity and who know that whatever is unjust bears with it a germ of destruction. But this impulse, it is melancholy to add, will be powerless if the union of the planters, if the colonial assemblies or legislatures, fail to adopt the same views and to act by a well-concerted plan having for its ultimate aim the cessation of slavery in the West Indies.

By the end of February, 1801, Bonpland and Humboldt had completed the observations they wanted to make in Cuba. They had studied the geological formations of the island together with its mineral resources. They had observed the distribution of plants and added to their plant collections. They had surveyed Cuba's climate, soil, and agricultural production (especially coffee, tobacco, and sugar). They had studied its people, their different origins, and the living conditions of freedmen and slaves. Never before in history had a country been surveyed so thoroughly in terms of its people and resources. Humboldt was laying the foundations of a new science—economic geography. In addition, Humboldt corrected the longitude of Havana, which, though a great seaport, had been incorrectly placed on the maps.

They were just about to proceed to Vera Cruz in order to cross Mexico and take a ship for the Philippines when the newspapers announced that the expedition of Captain Baudin had left France for Cape Horn. It was to proceed up the coasts of Chile and Peru and then cross the Pacific to Australia. To join this expedition Humboldt and Bonpland needed to get to the west coast of South America.

PREPARING TO LEAVE HAVANA

On leaving Spain, I had promised to rejoin the expedition wherever I could reach it. Bonpland and I resolved instantly to divide our herbals into three portions, to avoid exposing to the risks of a long voyage the objects we had obtained with so much difficulty on the banks of the Orinoco, the Atabapo, and the Río Negro. We sent one collection by way of England to Germany, another by way of Cádiz to France, and a third remained at Havana. We had reason to congratulate ourselves on this foresight: each collection contained nearly the same species, and no precautions were neglected to have the cases, if taken by English or French vessels, remitted to Sir Joseph Banks [a botanist and president of England's leading scientific body, The Royal Society of London] or to the professors of natural history at the Museum of Paris.

It happened, fortunately, that the manuscripts which I at first intended to send with the collection to Cádiz were not entrusted to our much esteemed friend and fellow traveler, Friar Juan Gonzales, of the order of the Observance of St. Francis, who had followed us to Havana with the view of returning to Spain. He left the island of Cuba soon after us, but the vessel in which he sailed foundered on the coast of Africa, and the cargo and crew were all lost. By this event we lost some of the duplicates of our herbals and, what was more important, all the insects which Bonpland had collected with great difficulty during our voyage to the Orinoco and the Río Negro.

By a singular fatality, we remained two years in the Spanish colonies without receiving a single letter from Europe; and those which arrived in the three following years made no mention of what we had transmitted. The reader may imagine my uneasiness for the fate of a journal which contained astronomical observations and barometrical measurements of which I had not made any copy. After having visited New Granada [Colombia], Peru, and Mexico, and just when I was preparing to leave the New Continent, I happened at a public library of Philadelphia to cast my eyes on a scientific publication, in which I found these words: "Arrival of M. de Humboldt's manuscripts at his brother's house in Paris, by way of Spain!" I could scarcely suppress an exclamation of joy.

While Monsieur Bonpland labored day and night to divide and put our collections in order, a thousand obstacles arose to impede our departure. There was no vessel in the port of Havana that would convey us to Porto Bello [seaport on the Isthmus of Panama near modern Colón] or Cartagena [seaport of Colombia]. The persons I consulted seemed to take pleasure in exaggerating the difficulties of the passage of the isthmus and the dangerous voyage from Panama to Guayaquil and from Guayaquil to Lima and Valparaíso. Not being able to find a passage in any neutral vessel, I hired a Catalonian sloop lying at Batabano, which was to be at my disposal to take me either to Porto Bello or Cartagena, according as the gales of Saint Martha might permit.

CHAPTER EIGHT

ACROSS THE ANDES

Back in South America, at Cartagena, Humboldt and Bonpland had to decide whether to get around to the Pacific coast by sea, except for the short trip across the Isthmus of Panama, or to go by land across the Andes to a Pacific port where they might join Captain Baudin.

The sea voyage from Panama to the port of Guayaquil in Ecuador would be difficult if a long delay in getting a vessel prevented them from leaving before wind and current turned against them.

Humboldt wanted to take the sea route for only one reason. He was interested in the best location for a canal across the Isthmus of Panama that would connect the Atlantic and Pacific oceans. One possible route was from Porto Bello to Panama City along the course of the Chagres River. But no one had ever measured the height of the mountains separating the two oceans at this point. If the mountains were low, this narrow part of the isthmus would be the most suitable place for a canal.

Humboldt was not able to survey the isthmus, but he did explore another large section of South America because Bonpland and he finally chose the overland route.

From Cartagena, they sent their heaviest instruments, many books, and some of their collections by sea to the Ecuador port of Guayaquil. Then they left for the Mag-

ACROSS THE ANDES

dalena River. On the night of April 21, 1801, they em-
barked in a native Indian canoe.

Ahead lay hundreds of miles of unexplored jungle.
The course of the river had never been charted, and
Humboldt devoted himself to this task. The whole area
was sparsely inhabited, and in one stretch of 120 miles
they found no dwelling place of any kind. By day the
forest was hot and humid; by night the sky was ablaze
with almost incessant thunderstorms.

It took fifty-five days for the Indian paddlers to get
them up the Magdalena River to the eastern foot of the
Andes. Then they hired mules and set out by pack train
for Quito. It was 450 miles away in a straight line, but
because of the rivers and the mountain passes, together
with special places they wanted to visit, they would have
to travel several times that distance.

To begin with, they had to make a big detour in order
to visit the renowned botanist Don José Celestino Mutis,
who lived in Bogotá. This would give them the opportu-
nity to compare their botanical notes and plant collections
with his. Word was sent ahead that they were coming.

TRIUMPHAL PROCESSION AT BOGOTÁ

OUR ARRIVAL at Santa Fé [Bogotá] resembled a triumphal pro-
cession. The archbishop sent his carriage to meet us, and with
it came the persons of greatest distinction in the capital. A
dinner was provided for us at some distance from the city, and
we proceeded with a retinue of more than sixty persons on
horseback. As the object of our coming was known to be a visit
to Mutis, who, on account of his great age, high position at
court, and personal character, is held in the greatest estimation

by all classes here, a certain degree of ceremony was accorded to our reception, that through us the inhabitants might do him honor. As the viceroy is forbidden by etiquette to entertain any guest at his own table in the capital, he invited us to dine with him at his country house at Fucha. Mutis had prepared a house for us in his own neighborhood, and received us with the utmost cordiality and friendship. He is an excellent old man, nearly seventy-two years of age; he has been in holy orders, and is possessed of considerable wealth. The king pays annually 10,000 piastres toward the expenses of botanical research. Thirty artists have been engaged during the last fifteen years in painting under the superintendence of Mutis; he has from 2,000 to 3,000 drawings in large portfolios, which are executed like miniature paintings. He possesses the largest botanical library I have ever seen, excepting that of Banks in London. . . .

From Bogotá the travelers recrossed the Magdalena River to Ibagué. From there, with twelve oxen to carry their baggage, they set out on foot for Cartago, over the worst pass in the Andes.

THE MOUNTAIN OF QUINDÍO

THE MOUNTAIN of Quindío is considered the most difficult passage in the Cordilleras of the Andes. It is a thick, uninhabited forest which in the finest season cannot be traversed in less than ten or twelve days. Not even a hut is to be seen, nor can any means of subsistence be found. Travelers at all times of the year furnish themselves with a month's provisions, since it often happens that, by the melting of the snows and the sudden swell of the torrents, they find themselves so cir-

After a sketch by Humboldt

QUINDÍO PASS

cumstanced that they can descend neither on the side of Cartago nor that of Ibagué. The highest point of the road, the
Garito del Paramo, is 11,435 feet above the level of the sea. . . .

The pathway which forms the passage of the Cordilleras is
only twelve to sixteen inches wide and has the appearance in
several places of a gallery dug and left open to the sky. In this
part of the Andes, as in almost every other, the rock is covered
with a thick stratum of clay. The streamlets which flow down
the mountains have hollowed out gullies about twenty feet
deep. Along these crevices, which are full of mud, the traveler
is forced to grope his passage, the darkness of which is increased by the thick vegetation that covers the opening above.
The oxen, which are the beasts of burden commonly made
use of in this country, can scarcely force their way through
these galleries, some of which are more than a mile long. If
perchance the traveler meets them in one of these passages, he
finds no means of avoiding them but by turning back and
climbing the earthen wall which borders the crevice and keeping himself suspended by laying hold of the roots which penetrate to this depth from the surface of the ground.

We traversed the mountain of Quindío in the month of
October, 1801, on foot, followed by twelve oxen which carried
our collections and instruments, amidst a deluge of rain to
which we were exposed during the last three or four days in
our descent on the western side of the Cordilleras. The road
passes through a country full of bogs and covered with bam-
boos. Our shoes were so torn by the prickles which shoot out
from the roots of these gigantic grasses that we were forced,
like all other travelers who dislike being carried on men's
backs, to go barefooted. This circumstance, the continual
humidity, the length of the passage, the muscular force re-

quired to tread in a thick and muddy clay, the necessity of fording deep torrents of icy water render this journey extremely fatiguing. But, however painful, it is accompanied by none of those dangers with which the credulity of the people alarm travelers. The road is narrow, but the places where it skirts precipices are very rare. . . .

As few persons in easy circumstances travel on foot in these climates through roads so difficult during fifteen or twenty days together, they are carried by men in chairs tied on their backs, for in the present state of the passage of Quindío it would be impossible to go on mules. They talk in this country of going on a man's back (andar en carguero) as we mention going on horseback. No humiliating idea is annexed to the trade of cargueroes, and the men who follow this occupation are not Indians but mulattoes and sometimes even whites. It is often curious to hear these men, with scarcely any covering and following a profession which we should consider so disgraceful, quarreling in the midst of a forest because one has refused the other, who pretends to have a whiter skin, the pompous title of "don," or of "su merced" [His Honor].

The usual load of a carguero is six or seven *arrobas* (165–195 pounds). Those who are very strong carry as much as nine arrobas. When we reflect on the enormous fatigue to which these miserable men are exposed, journeying eight or nine hours a day over a mountainous country; when we know that their backs are sometimes as raw as those of beasts of burden, and that travelers have often the cruelty to leave them in the forests when they fall sick; that they earn by a journey from Ibagué to Cartago only twelve or fourteen piastres in a space of fifteen and sometimes even twenty-five or thirty days, we are at a loss to conceive how this employment of a carguero, one of the most painful which can be undertaken by man, is eagerly embraced by all the robust young men who live at the foot of the mountains. The taste for wandering and vagabond life, the idea of a certain independence amidst forests, leads them to prefer this employment to the sedentary and monotonous labor of cities.

Among the carriers, those who have a sure foot and easy step are known and recommended to travelers. It is distressing to hear the qualities of man spoken of in terms by which we are accustomed to denote the gait of mules and horses. The persons who are carried in a chair by a carguero must remain several hours motionless and leaning backward; the least motion is sufficient to throw down the carrier, and his fall would be so much the more dangerous as the carguero, too confident in his skill, chooses the most rapid declivities or crosses a torrent on a narrow and slippery trunk of a tree. These accidents are, however, rare, and those which happen must be attributed to the imprudence of travelers who, frightened at a false step of the carguero, leap down from their chairs.

Having negotiated the Quindío Pass to Cartago, Humboldt and Bonpland began the next lap of their journey south to Popayán. The worst trip of all lay ahead—that from Popayán in southwest Colombia to Quito in Ecuador. Humboldt wrote a brief description of this in a letter to his brother.

THE ROAD TO QUITO

THE GREATEST difficulties of our journey lay yet before us between Popayán and Quito. We had to cross the Paramos of

Pasto in the rainy season, which had already set in. "Paramo" is the name given in the Andes to those desert regions where, at a height of about 12,000 feet above the sea, all vegetation ceases and the cold is so intense as to penetrate to the very bones. To avoid the heat of the valley of the Patía, where malaria exists to such an extent that one night spent within its precincts may engender a fever known among the Spaniards as the "calentura de Patía," lasting from three to four months, we crossed over the peak of the Cordilleras through a pass abounding with frightful precipices to Almager, whence we proceeded to Pasto, situated at the foot of a terrific volcano.

It would hardly be possible to picture a more horrible road than that by which access is obtained to this little town, where we spent Christmas (1801), and where we were welcomed by the inhabitants with a touching hospitality. Thick woods were interspersed with morasses in which the mules sank up to the girths, and narrow paths wound through such clefts in the rocks that one could almost fancy one was entering the gallery of a mine, while the road was paved with the bones of mules which had perished through cold or fatigue.

The whole province of Pasto . . . consists of a frozen mountain plateau, almost above the limit of vegetation and surrounded by volcanoes and solfataras [vents], from which wreaths of smoke continually issue. The unfortunate inhabitants of these regions live almost entirely on potatoes, and when this crop fails, as it did last year, they are obliged to retreat to the mountains, where they live upon the achupalla . . . , a small tree of which they eat the stem. As this tree serves also for food to the bears of the Andes, it is often only by contending with these animals that they can possess themselves of the only sustenance afforded by nature to man at this elevated region. . . . At length, after being wet through by torrents of rain night and day for two months and nearly drowned in the town of Ibarra by the sudden rise of the water during an earthquake, we reached Quito on the 6th of January, 1802.

QUITO

THE TOWN of Quito is handsome, but the sky is frequently overcast. The mountains in the neighborhood show no appearance of vegetation, and the cold is considerable.

The great earthquake of the 4th of February, 1797, by which the whole province was convulsed and some 40,000 persons instantaneously killed, has in every way proved a most disastrous event. . . . Since that calamity, earthquakes are of frequent occurrence, and occasionally the shocks are of great violence. It seems probable that the whole of the more elevated portion of the province is one vast volcano, and that the so-called mountains of Cotopaxi and Pichincha are but small peaks, the craters of which constitute the . . . [chimneys] of vast subterranean fires. The truth of this hypothesis has unfortunately been only too clearly demonstrated by the earthquake of 1797, for the earth then opened in all directions, casting forth sulphur, water, and so on.

Notwithstanding the dangers by which the inhabitants of Quito are surrounded and the apprehensions to which they must frequently be exposed, they are a gay, lively, and amiable people. The town breathes only an atmosphere of luxury and voluptuousness, and perhaps nowhere is there a population so entirely given up to the pursuit of pleasure. Thus can man accustom himself to sleep in peace on the brink of a precipice.

We remained in the province of Quito for nearly eight months—from the beginning of January till August, 1802—

and spent the time in visiting the principal volcanoes. We examined in succession Pichincha, Cotopaxi, Antisana, and Ilinica, devoting about a fortnight or three weeks to each and returning between times to the capital; finally, on the 9th of June we started for the ascent of Chimborazo.

Chimborazo's great snow-capped summit must have been a challenge to Humboldt's sense of adventure. But it was a scientific challenge, too. How high was the mountain? No one really knew, but it was thought to be the highest in the world. The Alps were partly known, the Himalayas not at all. Humboldt, Bonpland, and Carlos Montúfar reached a height of 19,286 feet, the highest man had ever climbed. We know now that the peak is 20,577 feet—277 feet higher than Mount McKinley in Alaska. It was not until thirty years later that an English party in the Himalayas climbed higher than Humboldt and his companions.

But Humboldt achieved much more than a world mountain-climbing record. Once again, as in Tenerife in the Canary Islands and in his climbs of various mountain peaks in Venezuela, he passed from lowlands to snowy peaks and noted a curious fact: the mountain was divided into zones. The temperature, the amount of rain and wind, and the soil changed as he climbed. As these conditions changed, the plants changed. Palms and fruit trees gave way to forests of ferns and rubber trees. Above these came evergreen trees, such as pines. And near the top there were only grasses and alpine plants.

Humboldt connected this plant distribution on mountains to something else he had observed. Plants change in the same way as one goes from the equator to the poles. A short trip up a mountain mirrored the changes from the tropics to the arctic regions. The distribution of plants depended upon the geography and climate of the region they inhabited. Humboldt also discovered in climbing Chimborazo and the other volcanic mountains of Ecuador that the mean temperature decreased 1°F. with each 300 feet of altitude, just as it decreased 1° with each de-

CHIMBORAZO MOUNTAIN

After a sketch by Humboldt

gree of latitude as one moved from the equator towards the poles.

CLIMBING CHIMBORAZO

UPON REACHING an elevation of 15,600 feet, the path became every moment narrower and steeper. The natives, with one exception, refused to accompany us farther and were deaf to entreaties and threatenings, maintaining they suffered more than we did from the rarity of the air. We were left alone— Bonpland, our estimable friend Carlos Montúfar, a younger son of the Marqués de Selvalegre, a half-caste Indian from the neighboring village of San Juan, and I.

By dint of great exertion and considerable patience we reached a greater height than we had dared to hope for, seeing we had been almost constantly enveloped in mist. In many places the ridge was not wider than from eight to ten inches! To our left was a precipice covered with snow, the surface of which shone like glass from the effects of frost. This thin sheet of ice was at an inclination of about thirty degrees. On the right was a fearful abyss, from eight hundred to one thousand feet deep, from the sides of which projected huge masses of naked rock. We leaned over rather more to this side than the other, for it seemed less to be dreaded than the precipice on our left, where the smooth sides afforded no opportunity of checking a fall by catching hold of projecting pieces of rock, and where the thin crust of ice furnished no security against being precipitated into the loose snow beneath.

The sloping surface of snow extended to such a distance that light pieces of dolerite [a volcanic rock], . . . when rolled down the incline, were lost sight of before reaching any resting place. . . .

The rock became more friable and the ascent increasingly difficult and dangerous. At certain places where it was very steep we were obliged to use both hands and feet, and the edges of the rock were so sharp that we were painfully cut, especially on our hands. In addition to this, I had for some weeks been suffering from a wound in my foot, caused by the repeated attacks of the *niguas* (sand fleas), which had been greatly aggravated by the fine pumice dust to which I had been exposed while taking measurements in the Llano de Tapia. The loose position of the stones upon the narrow ridge necessitated extreme caution, since many masses that appeared to be firmly attached proved to be only embedded in sand.

We advanced all the more slowly as every place that seemed insecure had first to be tested. Fortunately, the attempt to reach the summit of Chimborazo had been reserved for our last enterprise among the mountains of South America, so that we had gained some experience and knew how far we could rely on our own powers. It is a peculiar characteristic of all excursions on the Andes that beyond the line of perpetual snow Europeans are always left without guides just at the point where, from their complete ignorance of the locality, help is most needed. In everything Europeans are left to take the lead.

We could no longer see the summit, even by glimpses, and were therefore doubly anxious to ascertain how much of the ascent had still to be accomplished. We opened the tube barometer at a spot where the ridge was wide enough to allow two persons to stand side by side in safety. We were only at an elevation of 17,300 feet, therefore scarcely two hundred feet higher than we had attained three months previously upon the Antisana.

After an hour's cautious climbing the ridge of rock became less steep, but the mist unfortunately remained as thick as ever. One after another we all began to feel indisposed and experienced a feeling of nausea accompanied by giddiness which was far more distressing than the difficulty of breathing. . . . Blood exuded from the lips and gums, and the eyes became bloodshot. There was nothing particularly alarming to us in these symptoms, with which we had grown familiar by experience. . . . All these phenomena vary greatly in different individuals according to age, constitution, tenderness of the skin, and previous muscular exertion; yet in the same individual they constitute a kind of gauge for the amount of rarefaction of the atmosphere and for the absolute height that has been attained.

The stratum of mist which had hidden every distant object from our view began, notwithstanding the perfect calm, suddenly to dissipate—an effect probably due to the action of electricity. We recognized once more the dome-shaped summit of Chimborazo, now in close proximity. It was a grand and solemn spectacle, and the hope of attaining the object of all our efforts animated us with renewed strength.

The ridge of rock, only here and there covered with a thin sprinkling of snow, became somewhat wider, and we were hurrying forward with assured footsteps when our further progress was suddenly stopped by a ravine some 400 feet deep and sixty feet wide, which presented an insurmountable barrier to our undertaking. We could see clearly that the ridge on which we stood continued in the same direction on the other side of the ravine, but I was doubtful whether, after all, it really led to the summit. There was no means of getting round the cleft. On Antisana, after a night of severe frost, Bonpland had been able to travel a considerable distance upon the frozen surface of snow; but here the softness of the snowy mass prohibited such an attempt, and the nature of the declivity rendered it equally impossible to scale the sides.

It was now one o'clock in the afternoon. We fixed up the barometer with great care and found it stood at thirteen inches 11 2/10 lines. The temperature of the air was only three degrees below the freezing point, but, from our long residence in the tropics, even this amount of cold seemed quite benumbing. Our boots were wet through with snow water, for the sand which here and there lay on the mountain ridge was mixed with the remains of former snowdrifts. According to the barometric formula given by Laplace, we had now reached an elevation of 19,286 feet.

We remained but a short time in this dreary waste, for we were soon again enveloped in mist, which hung about us motionless. We saw nothing more of the summit of Chimborazo nor of the neighboring Snowy Mountains, far less of the elevated plain of Quito. We were isolated as in a balloon; a few rock lichens were to be observed above the line of perpetual snow at a height of 16,920 feet; the last green moss we noticed was growing about 2,600 feet lower. A butterfly was captured by Monsieur Bonpland at a height of 15,000 feet and a fly was observed 1,600 feet higher; both had been carried up into the higher regions of the atmosphere by the currents of air originating in the warmer plains beneath. We did not, however, see any condors, which are so numerous upon the Antisana and Pichincha, where in those vast solitudes, from being unaccustomed to the sight of man, they are wholly devoid of fear.

As the weather became increasingly threatening, we hurried down along the ridge of rock and, from the insecurity of our footing, found that even greater caution was necessary than during the ascent. We delayed no longer than sufficed for collecting fragments of rocks as specimens of the mountain structure. We foresaw that in Europe we should frequently be asked for "a fragment from Chimborazo."

When we were at a height of about 17,400 feet we encountered a violent hailstorm, which gave place to snow twenty minutes before passing the limit of perpetual snow, and the flakes were so thick that the ridge was soon covered several inches deep. The danger would indeed have been great had the snow overtaken us at a height of 18,000 feet. At a few minutes past two we reached the spot where we had left the mules.

During his year in and around Quito, Humboldt devoted considerable time and thought to the study of the old Indian civilizations. He had already found that the language of the Carib Indians he had met in northeast Venezuela combined "richness, grace, power, and tenderness." Now he studied the Inca language, which he found in ordinary use in this part of South America. It was "so rich in variety and delicacy of expression," he wrote, "that the young gentlemen, when making themselves agreeable to the ladies, usually adopt it after they have completely exhausted the vocabulary of the Spanish tongue."

He recognized that these languages provided evidence that there once reigned in America a higher civilization than existed at the time of the Spanish conquest after 1492. He found other proofs of the past glory of the Inca dynasty. The ancient Inca priests possessed amazing knowledge of astronomy, enabling them to make an accurate solar calendar. On the trip from Quito to Lima,

Humboldt saw for himself the magnificent roads built by the Incas. He was one of the first to give Europeans an adequate description of these mountain roads that resembled the finest roads of the ancient Romans.

LAND OF THE INCAS

AFTER HAVING sojourned for a whole year on the ridge of the Andes, between 4° north and 4° south latitude, amid the tablelands of New Granada, Pasto, and Quito, and consequently at an elevation varying between 8,500 and 15,000 feet above the level of the sea, it is delightful to descend gradually through the more genial climate of the Cinchona or Quina [quinine] woods of Loja into the plains of the upper Amazon.

There an unknown world unfolds itself, rich in magnificent vegetation. The little town of Loja has given its name to the most efficacious of all fever barks—quinine, or the *Cascarilla fina de Loja.* This bark is the precious produce of the tree which we have botanically described as the *Cinchona condaminea.* . . .

This beautiful tree, which is adorned with leaves five inches long and two broad, seems, when growing in the thick woods, as if striving to rise above its neighbors. The upper branches spread out, and, when agitated by the wind, the leaves have a peculiar reddish color and glistening appearance which is distinguished at a great distance. . . .

Descending from the mountain node of Loja south-southeast into the hot valley of the Amazon River, the traveler passes over the Paramos of Chulucanas, Guamani, and Yamoca. These Paramos are the mountainous deserts . . . which in the southern parts of the Andes are known by the name of *Puna,* a word belonging to the Quichua language. In most places their elevation is about 10,125 feet. They are stormy, frequently enveloped for several successive days in thick fogs or visited by terrific hailstorms. . . .

The solemn impression which is felt on beholding the deserts of the Cordilleras is increased in a remarkable and unsuspected manner by the circumstance that in these very regions there still exist wonderful remains of the great road of the Incas, that stupendous work by means of which communication was maintained among all the provinces of the empire along an extent of more than 1,000 miles. On the sides of this road, and at nearly equal distances apart, there are small houses built of well-cut freestone. These buildings, which answered the purpose of stations or caravanserais, are called tambos. . . . Some are surrounded by a sort of fortification; others were destined for baths and had arrangements for the conveyance of warm water; the larger ones were intended exclusively for the family of the sovereign. . . . While we journeyed onward for the distance of about four miles, our eyes were continually riveted on the grand remains of the Inca road, which was more than twenty feet wide. This road had a deep understructure and was paved with well-hewn blocks of . . . porphyry [volcanic rock containing crystals]. None of the Roman roads which I have seen in Italy, in the south of France, and in Spain appeared to me more imposing than this work of the ancient Peruvians. The Inca road is the more extraordinary since, according to my barometrical calculations, it is situated at an elevation of 13,258 feet above the level of the sea, a height exceeding that of the summit of the Peak of Tenerife by 1,000 feet. . . .

INCA ROAD

As the Peruvians had no wheeled carriages, these roads were constructed for the march of troops, for the conveyance of burdens borne by men, and for flocks of lightly laden llamas. Consequently, long flights of steps, with resting places, were formed at intervals in the steep parts of the mountains. Francisco Pizarro and Diego Almagro, in their expeditions to remote parts of the country, availed themselves with much advantage of the military roads of the Incas; but the steps just mentioned were formidable impediments in the way of the Spanish cavalry, especially as in the early period of the Conquest the Spaniards rode horses only and did not make use of the sure-footed mule, which, in mountainous precipices, seems to reflect on every step he takes. It was only at a later period that the Spanish troops were mounted on mules.

When, in the form of the earth, nature presents to man formidable difficulties to contend against, those very difficulties serve to stimulate the energy and courage of enterprising races of people. Under the despotic centralizing system of the Inca government, security and rapidity of communication, especially in relation to the movement of troops, were matters of urgent state necessity. Hence the construction of great roads and the establishment of very excellent postal arrangements by the Peruvians. . . .

The early Spanish conquistadores were filled with admiration on first beholding the roads and aqueducts of the Peruvians; yet not only did they neglect the preservation of those great works, but they even wantonly destroyed them. As a natural consequence of the destruction of the aqueducts, the soil was rendered infertile by the want of irrigation.

Nevertheless, those works, as well as the roads, were demolished for the sake of obtaining stones ready hewn for the erection of new buildings; and the traces of this devastation are more observable near the seacoast than on the ridges of the Andes or in the deeply cleft valleys with which that mountain chain is intersected.

During our long day's journey from . . . Zaulac to the valley of San Felipe we had to ford no less than twenty-seven times the Río de Guancabamba, which falls into the Amazon. We were compelled to do this on account of the numerous sinuosities of the stream, while on the brow of a steep precipice near us we had continually within our sight the vestiges of the rectilinear Inca road, with its tambos. The little mountain stream, the Río de Guancabamba, is not more than from 120 to 150 feet broad; yet so strong is the current that our heavily laden mules were in continual danger of being swept away by it. The mules carried our manuscripts, our dried plants, and all the other objects which we had been a whole year engaged in collecting; therefore, every time that we crossed the stream, we stood on one of the banks in a state of anxious suspense until the long train of our beasts of burden, eighteen or twenty in number, was fairly out of danger.

This same Río de Guancabamba, which in the lower part of its course has many falls, is the channel for a curious mode of conveying correspondence from the coast of the Pacific. For the expeditious transmission of the few letters that are sent from Trujillo to the province of Jaen de Bracamoros, they are dispatched by a swimming courier, or, as he is called by the people of the country, *el correo que nada*. This courier, who is usually a young Indian, swims in two days from Pomahuaca to Tomependa. . . . The few letters of which he is the bearer he carefully wraps up in a large cotton handkerchief, which he rolls round his head in the form of a turban. On arriving at those parts of the rivers in which there are falls or rapids, he lands and goes by a circuitous route through the woods. When wearied by long-continued swimming, he rests by throwing one arm on a plank of a light kind of wood [balsa]. . . . Sometimes the swimming courier takes with him a friend to bear him company. Neither troubles himself about provisions, as they are always sure of a hospitable reception in the huts which are surrounded by abundant fruit trees in the beautiful *huertas* [orchards] of Pucara and Cavico. . . .

The governor of Jaen de Bracamoros province assured me that letters sent by the singular water-post conveyance just mentioned are seldom either wet or lost. After my return from Mexico I myself received in Paris letters from Tomependa which had been transmitted in this manner. Many of the wild Indian tribes who dwell on the shores of the upper Amazon perform their journeys in a similar manner, swimming sociably down the stream in parties. On one occasion I saw the heads of thirty or forty individuals, men, women, and children, of the tribe of the Xibaros, as they floated down the stream on their way to Tomependa. The correo que nada returns by land, taking the difficult route of the Paramo del Paredon.

On approaching the hot climate of the basin of the Amazon, the aspect of beautiful and occasionally very luxuriant vegetation delights the eye. Not even in the Canary Islands nor on the warm coasts of Cumaná and Caracas had we beheld finer orange trees than those which we met with in the huertas de Pucara. They consisted chiefly of the sweet orange tree; the bitter orange trees were less numerous. These trees, laden with their golden fruit in thousands, attain there a height of between sixty and seventy feet; and their branches, instead of growing in such a way as to give the trees rounded tops or crowns, shoot straight up like those of the laurel. . . .

We remained seventeen days in the hot valley of the Marañon on the Amazon River. To proceed from thence to the coast of the Pacific it is necessary to cross the chain of the Andes. . . . Then, after having passed the ancient Cajamarca (the scene, 316 years ago, of the most sanguinary drama in the history of the Spanish Conquest, the route descends, with some interruptions, onto the Peruvian lowlands. . . .

The narrow path from Micuipampa to the ancient Inca city Cajamarca is difficult even for mules. The original name of the town was Cassamarca or Kazamarca—that is to say, the City

of Frost. . . . For the space of five or six miles the road led us
through a succession of paramos, where we were without intermission exposed to the fury of a boisterous wind and the
sharp, angular hail peculiar to the ridges of the Andes. The
height of the road is for the most part between 9,600 and
10,700 feet above sea level. There I had the opportunity of
making a magnetic observation of general interest—namely,
for determining the point where the north inclination of the
needle passes into the south inclination, and also the point at
which the traveler has to cross the magnetic equator.

Having at length reached the last of these mountain wilder-
nesses, the Paramo de Yanaguanga, the traveler joyfully looks
down into the fertile valley of Cajamarca. . . .

Descendants of the Inca still dwell in Cajamarca, amidst the
dreary architectural ruins of departed splendor. These descendants are the family of the Indian Cacique, or, as he is
called in the Quichua language, the *Curaca Astorpilca.* They
live in great poverty, but nevertheless contented and resigned
to their hard and unmerited fate. Their descent from Atahualpa [Inca prince who was burned at the stake by Pizarro in
1533] through the female line has never been a doubtful question in Cajamarca, but traces of beard would seem to indicate
some admixture of Spanish blood. . . .

The son of the Cacique Astorpilca, an interesting and amiable youth of seventeen, conducted us over the ruins of the ancient palace. Though living in the utmost poverty, his imagination was filled with images of the subterranean splendor
and the golden treasures which, he assured us, lay hidden beneath the heaps of rubbish over which we were treading. He
told us that one of his ancestors once blindfolded the eyes of

his wife and then, through many intricate passages cut in the rock, led her down into the subterranean gardens of the Inca. There the lady beheld, skillfully imitated in the purest gold, trees laden with leaves and fruit, with birds perched on their branches. . . . The husband commanded his wife not to touch any of these enchanted treasures, reminding her that the period fixed for the restoration of the Inca empire had not yet arrived, and that whosoever should touch any of the treasures would perish that same night.

These golden dreams and fancies of the youth were founded on recollections and traditions transmitted from remote times. Golden gardens such as those alluded to have been described by various writers who allege that they actually saw them. . . .

The son of Astorpilca assured me that underground, a little to the right of the spot on which I then stood, there was a large datura tree, or guanto, in full flower, exquisitely made of gold wire and plates of gold, and that its branches overspread the Inca's chair. The morbid faith with which the youth asserted his belief in this fabulous story made a profound and melancholy impression on me. These illusions are cherished among the people here, affording them consolation amidst great privation and earthly suffering. I said to the lad, "Since you and your parents so firmly believe in the existence of these gardens, do you not, in your poverty, sometimes feel a wish to dig for the treasures that lie so near you?" The young Peruvian's answer was so simple and so expressive of the quiet resignation peculiar to the aboriginal inhabitants of the country that I noted it down in Spanish in my journal. "Such a desire," said he, "never comes to us. My father says it would be sinful. If we had the golden branches, with all their golden fruits, our white neighbors would hate us and injure us. We have a little field and good wheat." Few of my readers will, I trust, be displeased that I have recalled here the words of young Astorpilca and his golden dreams.

An idea generally spread and firmly believed among the natives is that it would be criminal to dig up and take possession of treasures which may have belonged to the Incas, that such a proceeding would bring misfortune upon the whole Peruvian race. . . .

We remained five days in the capital of the Inca Atahualpa, which at that time numbered only 7,000 or 8,000 inhabitants. Our departure was delayed by the necessity of obtaining a great number of mules to convey our collections, and of selecting careful guides to conduct us across the chain of the Andes to the entrance of the long but narrow Peruvian sandy desert called the Desierto de Sechura. Our route across the Cordilleras lay from northeast to southwest.

FIRST VIEW OF THE PACIFIC

AFTER HAVING traveled for eighteen months without intermission within the restricted boundaries of the interior of a mountainous country, we felt an ardent desire to enjoy a view of the open sea, a desire which was heightened by repeated disappointments. . . . While we toiled along the ridges of the mighty mountain with expectation on the stretch, our guides, who were not very well acquainted with the way, repeatedly assured us that after proceeding another mile our hopes would be fulfilled. The stratum of mist in which we were enveloped seemed sometimes to disperse for a moment, but whenever that happened our view was bounded by intervening heights.

The desire which we feel to behold certain objects is not

excited solely by their grandeur, their beauty, or their importance. In each individual this desire is interwoven with
pleasing impressions of youth, with early predilections for
particular pursuits, with the inclination for traveling, and the
love of an active life. In proportion as the fulfillment of a wish
may have appeared improbable, its realization affords the
greater pleasure. The traveler enjoys, in anticipation, the
happy moment when he shall first behold the constellation of
the Cross and the Magellanic clouds circling over the South
Pole; when he shall come in sight of the snow of the Chimborazo, and of the column of smoke ascending from the volcano of Quito; when, for the first time, he shall gaze on a
grove of tree ferns or on the wide expanse of the Pacific
Ocean. The days on which such wishes are fulfilled mark
epochs in life and create indelible impressions, exciting feelings which require not to be accounted for by any process of
reasoning.

The longing I felt to behold the Pacific from the lofty ridges
of the Andes was mingled with recollections of the interest
with which, as a boy, I had dwelt on the narrative of the ad-
venturous expedition of Vasco Nuñez de Balboa. That happy
man, whose track Pizarro followed, was the first to behold,
from the heights of Quarequa on the Isthmus of Panama, the
eastern part of the great "South Sea.". . .

After passing over many undulations of ground on the
rugged mountain ridges, we at length reached the highest
point of the Alto de Guangamarca. The sky, which had so long
been obscured, now suddenly brightened. A sharp southwest
breeze dispersed the veil of mist, and the dark blue canopy of
heaven was seen between the narrow lines of the highest
feathery clouds. . . .

We now, for the first time, commanded a view of the Pacific. We saw it distinctly, reflecting along the line of the coast an immense mass of light and rising in immeasurable expanse until bounded by the clearly defined horizon. The delight which my companions, Bonpland and Carlos Montúfar, shared with me in viewing this prospect caused us to forget to open the barometer on the Alto de Guangamarca. According to a calculation which we made at a place somewhat lower down, the point at which we first gained a view of the ocean must have been at no greater an elevation than between 9,380 and 9,600 feet.

The view of the Pacific was solemnly impressive to one who, like myself, was greatly indebted, for the formation of his mind and the direction given to his tastes and aspirations, to one of the companions of Captain Cook. I made known the general outline of my traveling schemes to George Forster when I had the advantage of visiting England under his guidance. . . . Forster's charming pictures of Otaheite [Tahiti] had awakened throughout northern Europe a deep interest (mingled with a sort of romantic longing) in favor of the islands of the Pacific Ocean. At that period, when but few Europeans had been fortunate enough to visit those islands, I cherished the hope of seeing them at least in part; for the object of my visit to Lima was twofold: first, to observe the transit of Mercury over the solar disk, and, secondly, to fulfill a promise I had made to Captain Baudin on my departure from Paris. This promise was to join him in the circumnavigatory voyage which he was to undertake as soon as the French Republic could furnish the necessary funds. . . .

But Captain Baudin's expedition took quite a different

course from that which had been expected and announced. Instead of proceeding by the way of Cape Horn, as had been intended at the time when it was agreed that Bonpland and I should join it, the expedition sailed round the Cape of Good Hope. One of the objects of my visit to Peru and of my last journey across the chain of the Andes was thus thwarted.

But I had the singular good fortune, at a very unfavorable season of the year in the misty regions of lower Peru, to enjoy a clear, bright day. In Callao [seaport of Lima] I observed the passage of Mercury over the sun's disk, an observation of some importance in aiding the accurate determination of the longitude of Lima and of the southwestern part of the New Continent. Thus, amidst the serious troubles and disappointments of life there may often be found a grain of consolation.

CHAPTER NINE

TO MEXICO AND THE UNITED STATES

In December, 1802, Humboldt and Bonpland embarked from Callao on a sailing vessel headed for Acapulco on the west coast of Mexico. They were accompanied by Don Carlos Montúfar, whom they had found such a good and resourceful companion when he climbed Chimborazo with them.

On the long voyage Humboldt surveyed the coasts of Peru and Ecuador. He also occupied himself with measuring the temperature and rate of flow of the cold current that bathes these shores. This has been known as the Humboldt Current ever since.

It was the end of March, 1803, when they reached Mexico, the grandest and richest of all the Spanish possessions in the New World, the "Kingdom of New Spain." Both Humboldt and Bonpland were terribly disappointed at having had to give up the projected trip across the Pacific with Baudin, but Humboldt now was eager to get back to Europe to catch up with the latest scientific developments. Besides, his instruments were in such bad shape from four years of rough wear that they would be useless for further work in Mexico. This made the travelers decide to stay only a few months.

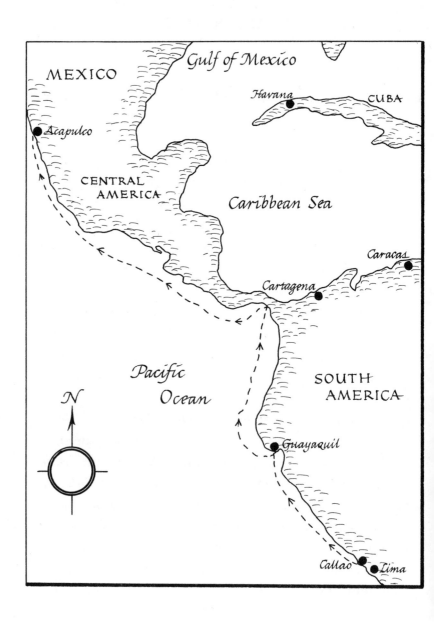

To Mexico

After correcting the position of Acapulco on existing maps by more accurate astronomical observations, they set out for Mexico City by way of Taxco, a town famous for its silver mines. In Mexico City the director of the School of Mines, who had been a pupil of Humboldt's old geology teacher, Abraham Werner, loaned him a new set of instruments. As a result, Humboldt stayed in Mexico a whole year.

Humboldt studied everything *in Mexico, from mining methods to banana cultivation, from Aztec monuments and hieroglyphics to the Indian population. He measured the height of Popocatepetl Mountain and studied the formation of Mexican volcanoes. Years later he published a book entitled* Political Essay on the Kingdom of New Spain, *the first modern work on the economic geography of a whole country. It included a study of Mexico's natural resources and how they were utilized.*

When William Prescott, famous American historian, started his research on the civilization of the Aztecs and Incas and their conquest by the Spaniards, he found Humboldt a "mine of knowledge" and "the first, almost the last, writer on these topics" who made his theories conform to the facts instead of the other way round.

Here are some of Humboldt's observations on the people and geology of Mexico.

THE MEXICAN INDIANS

THE INDIANS of New Spain [Mexico] bear a general resemblance to those who inhabit Canada, Florida, Peru, and Brazil. They have the same swarthy and copper color, flat and smooth hair, small beard, squat body, long eye with the corner directed up towards the temples, prominent cheekbones, thick lips, and an expression of gentleness in the mouth, strongly contrasted with a gloomy and severe look. The American race ... is the least numerous, but it occupies the greatest space on the globe. Over a million and a half of square leagues, from the Tierra del Fuego islands to the St. Lawrence River and Bering Strait, we are struck at the first glance with the general resemblance in the features of the inhabitants. We think we perceive that they all descend from the same stock, notwithstanding the enormous diversity of language which separates them from one another. However, when we reflect more seriously on this family likeness, after living longer among the indigenous Americans, we discover that celebrated travelers who could only observe a few individuals on the coasts have singularly exaggerated the analogy of form among the Americans. . . .

The same style of feature exists, no doubt, in both Americas; but those Europeans who have sailed on the great rivers Orinoco and Amazon and have had occasion to see a great number of tribes assembled under the monastical hierarchy in the missions must have observed that the American race contains nations whose features differ as essentially from one another as the numerous varieties of the Caucasian race, the Circassians, Moors, and Persians, differ from one another. The tall form of the Patagonians, who inhabit the southern extremity of the New Continent, is again found by us, as it were, among the Caribs who dwell in the plains from the delta of the Orinoco to the sources of the Río Blanca. What a difference between the figure, physiognomy, and physical constitution of these Caribs, who ought to be accounted one of the most robust nations on the face of the earth, and the squat bodies of the

After a sketch by Humboldt

MEXICAN INDIANS

Chayma Indians of the province of Cumaná! What a differ-ence of form between the Indians of Tlaxcala and the Lipans and Chichimecks of the northern part of Mexico!

As to the moral faculties of the Indians, it is difficult to ap-preciate them with justice if we only consider this long-op-pressed caste in their present state of degradation. The better sort of Indians, among whom a certain degree of intellectual culture might be supposed, perished in great part at the com-mencement of the Spanish Conquest, the victims of European ferocity. The Christian fanaticism broke out in a particular manner against the Aztec priests, and the *teopixqui,* or minis-ters of the divinity, and all those who inhabit the *teocalli,* or houses of God, who might be considered as the depositories of the historical, mythological, and astronomical knowledge of the country. . . .

The monks burned the hieroglyphical paintings by which every kind of knowledge was transmitted from generation to generation. The people, deprived of these means of instruction, were plunged into an ignorance so much the deeper as the missionaries were unskilled in the Mexican languages and could substitute few new ideas in place of the old. The Indian women who had preserved any share of fortune chose rather to ally with the conquerors than to share the contempt in which the Indians were held. The Spanish soldiers were so much the more eager for these alliances as very few European women had followed the army. The remaining natives then consisted only of the most indigent race: poor cultivators, artisans, among whom were a great number of weavers; porters, who were used like beasts of burden; and especially of those dregs of the people, those crowds of beggars, who bore witness to the imperfections of the social institutions and the existence of feudal oppression. . . . How shall we judge, then, from these miserable remains of a powerful people, the degree of cultivation to which it had risen from the twelfth to the sixteenth century, and the intellectual development of which it is capable? If all that remained of the French or German nation were a few poor agriculturists, could we read in their features that they belonged to nations which had produced a Descartes and a Clairaut, a Kepler and a Leibnitz?

We observe that even in Europe the lower people, for whole centuries, make very slow progress in civilization. The peasant of Brittany or Normandy and the inhabitant of the north of Scotland differ very little at this day from what they were in the time of Henry IV and James I. . . . How can any great change take place in the Indians when they are kept insulated in villages in which the whites dare not settle, when the difference of language places an almost insurmountable barrier between them and the Europeans, when they are oppressed by magistrates chosen through political considerations from their own number, and, in short, when they can expect moral and civil improvement only from a man who talks to them of mysteries, dogmas, and ceremonies, of the end of which they are ignorant? . . .

The Americans, like the Hindus and other nations who have longed groaned under a civil and military despotism, adhere to their customs, manners, and opinions with extraordinary obstinacy. I say opinions, for the introduction of Christianity has produced almost no other effect on the Indians of Mexico than to substitute new ceremonies, the symbols of a gentle and humane religion, for the ceremonies of a sanguinary worship. This change from old to new rites was the effect of constraint and not of persuasion, and was produced by political events alone. In the New Continent as well as in the Old, half-civilized nations were accustomed to receive from the hands of the conqueror new laws and new divinities; and the vanquished Indian gods appeared to them to yield to the gods of the strangers.

In such a complicated mythology as that of the Mexicans, it was easy to find out an affinity between Aztec divinities and the divinity of the east. Cortez even very artfully took advantage of a popular tradition according to which the Spaniards were merely the descendants of King Quitzalcoatl, who left Mexico for countries situated in the east to carry among them civilization and laws. The ritual books composed by the Indians in hieroglyphics at the beginning of the conquest evidently show that at that period Christianity was confounded with the Mexican mythology: the Holy Ghost is identified with the sacred eagle of the Aztecs. The missionaries not only tolerated, they even favored to a certain extent, this amalgamation of ideas, by means of which the Christian worship was more easily introduced among the natives. They persuaded them that the gospel had, in very remote times, been already preached in America; and they investigated its traces in the Aztec ritual. . . .

These circumstances explain why the Mexican Indians, notwithstanding the obstinacy with which they adhere to whatever is derived from their fathers, have so easily forgotten their ancient rites. Dogma has not succeeded to dogma, but ceremony to ceremony. The natives know nothing of religion but the exterior forms of worship. Fond of whatever is connected with a prescribed order of ceremonies, they find in the Christian religion particular enjoyments. The festivals of the church, the fireworks with which they are accompanied, the processions mingled with dances and whimsical disguises are a most fertile source of amusement for the lower Indians. In these festivals the national character is displayed in all its individuality. Everywhere the Christian rites have assumed the shades of the country where they have been transplanted. In the Philippine and Mariana islands the natives of the Malay race have incorporated them with the ceremonies which are peculiar to themselves; and in the province of Pasto, on the ridge of the Andes, I have seen Indians, masked and adorned with small tinkling bells, perform savage dances around the altar while a monk of St. Francis elevated the host.

Accustomed to a long slavery, as well under the domination of their own sovereigns as under that of the first conquerors, the natives of Mexico patiently suffer the vexations to which they are frequently exposed by the whites. They oppose to them only a cunning, veiled under the most deceitful appearances of apathy and stupidity. As the Indian can very rarely revenge himself on the Spaniards, he delights in making common cause with them for the oppression of his own fellow citizens. Harassed for ages and compelled to a blind obedience, he wishes to tyrannize in his turn. The Indian villages are governed by magistrates of the copper-colored race, and an Indian alcalde exercises his power with so much the greater severity because he is sure of being supported by the priest or the Spanish *subdelegado*. Oppression produces everywhere the same effects: it everywhere corrupts the morals.

THE INDIAN LOVE OF FLOWERS

THE MEXICAN Indians have preserved the same taste for flowers that Cortez found in his time. A nosegay was the most valuable treat which could be made to the ambassadors who visited the court of Montezuma. This monarch and his predecessors had collected a great number of rare plants in the gardens of Istapalapan. . . . The taste for flowers undoubtedly indicates a relish for the beautiful, and we are astonished at finding it in a nation in which a sanguinary worship and the frequency of sacrifices appeared to have extinguished whatever related to the sensibility of the soul and kindness of affection.

In the great market place of Mexico [City] the native sells no peaches, nor bananas, nor roots, nor *pulque* (the fermented juice of the agave) without having his shop ornamented with flowers, which are renewed every day. The Indian merchant appears seated in a green enclosure. A hedge three feet high, formed of fresh herbs, particularly of grasses with delicate leaves, surrounds like a semicircular wall the fruits offered to public sale. . . .

The European . . . cannot help being struck with the care and elegance the natives display in distributing the fruits which they sell in small cages of very light wood. The *sapotilles* [plums], the *mammea* (apricots), pears, and raisins occupy the bottom, while the top is ornamented with fragrant flowers. This art of entwining fruits and flowers had its origin, perhaps, in that happy period when, long before the introduction of inhuman rites, the first inhabitants of Anahuac, like the Peruvians, offered up to the great spirit Teotle the first fruits of their harvest.

A VOLCANO IS BORN

THE VOLCANO of Jorullo was formed in the night of September 29, 1759. The great catastrophe in which this mountain rose from the earth, and by which the face of a considerable extent of ground was totally altered, was perhaps one of the most extraordinary physical changes in the history of our planet. Geology points out spots in the ocean where, within the last two thousand years, volcanic islets have arisen above the surface of the sea, as near the Azores, in the Aegean Sea, and on the south of Iceland. But it records no instance of a mountain of scoriae [lava] and ashes, 1,689 feet above the old level of the neighboring plains, suddenly formed in the center of a thousand small burning cones, thirty-six leagues [108 miles] from the seashore and forty-two leagues [126 miles] from any other active volcano. This phenomenon remained unknown to the mineralogists and natural philosophers of Europe, though it took place but fifty years ago and within six days' journey from the capital of Mexico. . . .

After a sketch by Humboldt

THE VOLCANO OF JORULLO

Until the middle of the eighteenth century, fields of sugar cane and indigo extended between two brooks called Cuitimba and San Pedro. They were bounded by basaltic mountains, the structure of which seems to indicate that all this country in remote periods had experienced the violent action of volcanoes. These fields, watered by artificial means, belonged to the estate of San Pedro de Jorullo, one of the largest and richest in the country.

In the month of June, 1759, fearful rumbling noises were accompanied by frequent earthquakes. These succeeded each other at intervals for fifty or sixty days and threw the inhabitants of the estate into the greatest consternation. From the beginning of September everything seemed perfectly quiet; then in the night of the 28th of that month the horrible

subterranean noise began again. The frightened Indians fled
to the mountains of Aguasarco. A space of three or four square
miles, known by the name of Malpays, rose up in the shape of
a bladder. . . .

Those who witnessed this grand catastrophe from the top of
Aguasarco assert that they saw flames issue out of the ground
for the space of more than half a league square; that fragments
of red-hot rocks were thrown up to prodigious heights; and
that through a thick cloud of ashes, illumined by the volcanic
fire, the softened crust of the earth was seen to swell up like
a stormy sea. The rivers of Cuitimba and San Pedro then precipitated themselves into the burning chasms. The decomposi-
tion of the water contributed to invigorate the flames. . . .
Thousands of small cones only two or three yards high, which
the Indians call ovens, issued from the raised dome of the
Malpays. Though the heat of these volcanic ovens has diminished greatly within these fifteen years according to the testi-
mony of the Indians, I found the thermometer rise to 203° F.
in the crevices that emitted steam. Each little cone is a chim-
ney from which vapor rises to the height of thirty-three to
forty-eight feet. In several a subterranean noise is heard like
that of some fluid boiling at no great depth.

Amid these ovens . . . six large hummocks rise from 1,320
to 1,650 feet above the old level of the plain. This is the
phenomenon of Monte Nuovo at Naples repeated several
times in a row of volcanic hills. The loftiest of these huge
hummocks is the great volcano of Jorullo. It is constantly
burning, and has thrown out on the north side an immense
quantity of scorified and basaltic lava, including fragments of
primitive rocks. These grand eruptions of the central volcano

continued till February, 1760. In the succeeding years they became gradually less frequent.

The Indians, alarmed by the horrible noise of the new volcano, at first deserted the villages for twenty or thirty miles round the plain of Jorullo. In a few months, however, they became accustomed to this terrifying spectacle. Having returned to their huts, they went to the mountains of Aguas-arco and Santa Ines to admire the streams of fire thrown out by an infinite number of large and small volcanic openings. . . .

Although the subterranean fire now appears far from violent and the Malpays and the great volcano begin to be covered with vegetables, we nevertheless found the surrounding air heated to such a degree by the action of the small ovens that the thermometer, at a great distance from the surface, rose in the shade as high as 109° F. This fact appears to prove that there is no exaggeration in the accounts of several old Indians who affirm that for many years after the first eruption the plains of Jorullo, even at a great distance from the scene of the explosion, were uninhabitable from the excessive heat which prevailed in them.

Humboldt drew interesting generalizations from his studies of Jorullo. Until the close of the eighteenth century all that was known of volcanoes was derived from observations made on two volcanic mountains of southern Italy, Vesuvius and Etna. These were regarded as typical of all volcanoes in the whole world. But the mighty volcanoes of Mexico and South America had not been studied. Humboldt's observations on these volcanoes led him to the conclusions that their action did not depend on slight causes located near the surface of the earth's crust, and that they were not sporadic phenomena occurring here or there accidentally.

He was dissatisfied with the scientists who picked up samples of rock from the mouths of burning volcanoes and merely described and classified them. He was concerned with broader questions, and felt that volcanic phenomena all over the world had to be examined and their relationships studied. As he put it, "It is only by considering these various relations under a general point of view, and tracing them over a great extent of the surface of the globe, through formations of rocks the most different, that we are led to abandon the supposition of trifling local causes. . . ."

In Mexico he had observed that there was a very narrow zone just above the 19th parallel in which all the volcanic mountains were located. They were on a line perpendicular to the Mexican Cordillera (mountain chain), and the new volcano of Jorullo was on a continuation of this same line that included the famous Popocatepetl. Humboldt figured from this that these volcanoes marked a deep interior crack in the earth's crust which stretched from east to west through a distance of 500 miles. Through this crack the volcanic fire made its way at different times, bursting the outer crust of rock from the coast of the Gulf of Mexico to the Pacific Ocean.

From his studies of three volcanoes on the tableland of Quito in the Andes he concluded that they were not separate and independent volcanoes, but constituted one gigantic volcanic hearth. The subterranean fire burst sometimes from one and sometimes from another of these openings.

Humboldt showed for the first time that volcanoes appeared in groups, almost always in a definite line, and represented fractures of the earth's crust that extended to great depths.

On March 7, 1804, Humboldt, Bonpland, and Montúfar set sail from Vera Cruz for Havana to pick up the collections they had left there in 1800. After two months in Cuba they sailed for the United States, arriving in Philadelphia twenty days later. Humboldt immediately wrote to President Thomas Jefferson, telling him that he would love to talk to him "as a friend of science" and because of the liberalism of his ideas.

Jefferson welcomed Humboldt in Washington and took him to his home, Monticello. For days they discussed science, Spanish America, and the great United States experiment in democracy. Humboldt's maps, charts, and figures were highly meaningful for the visionary Jefferson and his able Secretary of the Treasury, Albert Gallatin. If the mines of South America had produced more than five billion dollars' worth of gold and silver since the Conquest, what wealth did the Rocky Mountains of the western United States contain? Where was the exact boundary between Louisiana and New Spain, and what kind of people lived in this doubtful area? Humboldt answered many questions of interest to the young government of the United States. He was impressed by Jefferson's wisdom. Jefferson and Gallatin were amazed by the extraordinary range of Humboldt's knowledge.

Back in Philadelphia, Humboldt and his companions were entertained by renowned members of the American Philosophical Society, which had been founded by Benjamin Franklin.

On June 27 Humboldt wrote a farewell letter to Jefferson from Philadelphia: "My departure is scheduled for tomorrow. . . . I have had the honor to see the First Magistrate of this great republic living with the simplicity of a philosopher. . . . I leave with the consolation that the people of this great continent march with great strides toward the perfection of a social state, while Europe presents an immoral and melancholy spectacle."

At the end of June, Humboldt and his two companions sailed from Philadelphia for France. From Bordeaux, on August 1, 1804, he wrote a letter to his friend Karl Freiesleben describing the end of his journey and something of his scientific achievements.

BACK TO EUROPE

AFTER AN absence of five years I am once more upon European soil. We made the entrance of the Garonne two hours ago. We have been most highly favored in our voyage, accomplishing the passage from Philadelphia in twenty-seven days.

I left Mexico in February and sailed by way of Havana to North America, where I was loaded with marks of honor by Jefferson, the President of the States. My expeditions in both hemispheres, extending over a distance of 40,000 miles, have been favored by fortune to an almost unprecedented degree. I was never once ill, and I am now in better health, stronger in body, more industrious, and gayer in spirits than ever.

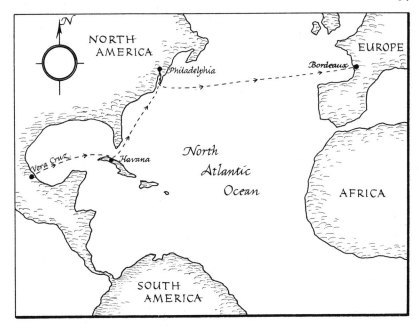

NORTH
AMERICA

EUROPE

Philadelphia

Bordeaux

North
Atlantic
Ocean

Vera Cruz

Havana

AFRICA

SOUTH
AMERICA

BACK TO EUROPE

I return laden with thirty cases of treasures of all kinds, botanical, geological, and astronomical, and it will take me years to bring out my great work. My sectional drawings of the Andes, based upon no less than 1,500 of my own measurements, a botanical atlas, and a geological pasigraphy [sign system], consisting of new symbols for expressing the various formations, will all interest you exceedingly.

I confess it was with a heavy heart that I bade farewell to the bright glories of a tropical clime. . . . As soon as I can get out of quarantine, I shall leave for Paris, that I may begin my work immediately. . . . I quite dread the first winter—everything will be so strange, and I shall be some time in settling down again. But I shall be consoled through everything by the thought of my safety.

EPILOGUE

HUMBOLDT'S LATER LIFE

HUMBOLDT WAS back in Paris. But Paris and all France had changed greatly since his departure. He had left France a republic, and returned to find it an empire, with Napoleon on the throne.

But even this momentous change in the political life of France did not affect Humboldt's triumphant welcome. Paris was still the hub of the scientific world, and all the great men of science gathered around him to hear from his own lips stories of his adventures and investigations. Some reports of his scientific feats had been read before learned societies while he was still in South America. Twice European papers had carried reports of his death. One report had him killed by savages on the Orinoco. Another announced his death from yellow fever at Acapulco. But now the great man was here in person, with his vast collections of plants, rocks, fossils, and animals. Scientific institutions vied with one another to organize receptions for Humboldt and Bonpland. The leading ladies of Parisian society competed to get the great Humboldt into their drawing rooms.

Humboldt's sister-in-law, Caroline, was in Paris at the time. In a letter to a friend she wrote, "The crowning pleasure of my visit here has been the happy return of our dear Alex and the gratification of witnessing the reception that has been accorded him. It has rarely fallen to the lot of any private individual to create so much excitement by his presence or infuse an interest so universal."

Humboldt was charmed with Parisian society and the attention he received, but he had an enormous task before him. He planned the publication of eleven volumes, based on his mountains of journals and notes as well as on his collections. The works were to be issued under the names of Humboldt and Bonpland and were to be brought out in French, German, English, Spanish, and Danish. But in what language should he write? German was his native tongue, but he thought he could write more correctly and elegantly in Spanish. He ended up writing in French. And the eleven works, which he thought he could get off his hands in a couple of years, turned out to be some thirty volumes, many of them huge, with nearly 1,500 maps and plates. They took thirty-five years to complete. Many other scientists, specialists in astronomy, magnetism, geology, and botany, were enlisted to help put the mammoth reports in order.

The pressure of all this work did not keep him from embarking on new scientific projects. During that first winter in Paris he spent months in laboratories investigating the chemical constitution of the atmosphere with the famous chemist Gay-Lussac.

By March of 1805 Humboldt felt it imperative to visit his brother, Wilhelm, in Rome, where Wilhelm was Prussian minister to the Papal court. At his brother's home Alexander met many of the artists and map-makers who later did the maps and illustrations for his published volumes.

In Rome he heard that the famous Italian volcano Vesuvius was showing signs of erupting. Immediately he left for Naples to observe for himself one of nature's strangest performances.

One of Humboldt's companions on the slopes of Vesuvius was a young South American he had met earlier in Paris. His name was Simón Bolívar and he was from Caracas, which Humboldt knew so well. They talked of Spanish rule in Latin America and together "made vows for the liberty and independence of the New Continent." Shortly afterward, Bolívar returned home and eventually became the leader of the revolutionary forces. He is known to this day as "The Liberator." Throughout Bolívar's stormy career he never forgot the debt he and all of South America owed to Humboldt, "whose learning," he wrote, "has done America more good than all of the conquerors." Humboldt was in a very real sense, Bolívar thought, "the discoverer of the New World."

From Italy Humboldt traveled to Germany, his native land. The king of Prussia showered him with honors. He was made an Honorary Member of the Royal Academy of Science and was awarded a pension. This he badly needed, for the publication of his works threatened to drain away his fortune. Humboldt worked hard in Berlin. He supervised the printing of his books, read papers before scientific gatherings, and did new research on the magnetism of the earth with the astronomer Oltmanns. But Humboldt was desolate in Berlin and longed to return to Paris.

Meanwhile, critical events were determining his future. Napoleon defeated Prussia at the Battle of Jena. The terms of the peace were hard. In the hope that Humboldt, with his broad contacts in France, could negotiate better terms for the Prussians, the king asked him to accompany Prince Wilhelm, the king's brother, to Paris.

Humboldt remained in Paris from 1808 till 1826. His energy was prodigious. He rose before eight o'clock in the morning, carried on his work at the scientific institute till seven in the evening, and then went out to relax in society. He traveled from reception to reception, telling stories from the inexhaustible fund of experience he had piled up in South America. By midnight he was back in his study, where he worked until two.

All of Paris came to know him. If a visitor to Paris took a seat in a carriage and gave Humboldt's address, the driver was sure to reply, "Ah, chez Monsieur Humboldt!" and from that moment he would view his passenger with interest.

Meanwhile, Humboldt was bringing out volume after volume of his South American travels. Although his own share of these reports was going along smoothly, he was having trouble with his dear friend Bonpland. Humboldt finally wrote to him in 1810:

> You do not send me a line on the subject of botany. I beg and beseech you to persevere until the work is completed. I am quite determined that the results of our expedition should not be lost, and if in the space of eight months it is not possible to produce more than ten plates, which is only what any botanist in Europe would prepare in a fortnight, there is no reason to expect the completion of the second volume of the *Plantes équinoxiales* under three years. . . . I therefore again beseech you, my dear Bonpland, to persevere in this undertaking to the end: it is an object of the highest importance, not only in the interests of science, but for the sake of your own reputation and the fulfillment of those engagements into which you entered with me in 1798. . . .

At the time, Bonpland was superintending the botanical gardens of the Empress Josephine. When she died in 1814,

Bonpland was unable to settle down to any other work, and two years later he sailed once again for South America. At Buenos Aires he became Professor of Natural History, but before long, while on a journey of exploration and botanical research, his party was attacked in a disputed area by the troops of the dictator of Paraguay. All his companions were killed, and Bonpland was wounded in the head with a saber, put in chains, and taken into the interior as a prisoner.

Humboldt did everything possible to obtain his friend's freedom. But Bonpland was not set free until nine years later. Upon his release he did not return to Europe, but settled down in the area in which he had been imprisoned. He lived there for thirty years, known only as "Don Amado." Unlike Humboldt, Bonpland had lost all ambition. He wrote to his old traveling companion that he was sorry for him, doomed as he was to a dreary life in Berlin. As for himself, he was happy in the society of his beloved plants, which, he said, "have been my companions through life."

Even while Humboldt was occupied in organizing and publishing the results of his travels, he dreamed of new ones. India, Tibet, the Himalayas—he had wanted to see them long before he set out for South America. How high were these mountains? No one knew. As far as was known, he had climbed the highest mountain in the world, Chimborazo. He studied Asian languages and read everything that had been published on Asia's climate, geology, and plants.

In 1811 an invitation came. Russia was preparing an expedition to Tibet, and Humboldt was invited to join it. He replied that he would, but on condition that he could make it part of a seven- or eight-year journey to the Asian tropics, to Lake Baikal and the volcanoes of the Kamchatka Peninsula.

Napoleon's invasion of Russia in 1812 put an end to that dream.

Seven years later the Prussian king planned to finance a trip to Asia for Humboldt. After preparations were completed and instruments secured, the journey had to be given up. Then in 1827 a letter came from the Russian Minister of Finance asking Humboldt's opinion on the use of platinum, which had just been discovered in the Ural Mountains, as a basis for coinage instead of gold. The letter casually added that "The Ural Mountains would well repay a visit from a man of scientific eminence."

Nothing more was needed. Humboldt was ready to go. But who would finance such a journey? The reply came that Emperor Nicholas wished Humboldt to make a scientific expedition to Siberia at the emperor's expense. Finally all was arranged, and on April 12, 1829, Humboldt, with two distinguished scientists he had invited, and with every conceivable kind of instrument and apparatus, set out from Berlin in two carriages for St. Petersburg.

After a week of royal entertainment there Humboldt and his two friends started across Russia. Humboldt was nearly sixty years old now. Thirty years before, he and Bonpland had walked from Marseille to Madrid. A few years later they had journeyed by foot and mule across Colombia, Ecuador, and Peru. Now he was riding in style! But he was still strong and nimble. When he wanted to make excursions into areas the carriages could not penetrate, Humboldt went on foot, climbing over high mountains without any sign of fatigue.

The Urals were rich in gold and platinum, but Humboldt predicted from their geologic similarity to the mountains of Brazil that diamonds would be discovered there as well. A few days after he wrote the Russian finance minister to this effect, diamonds were found near where Humboldt said they should be.

The party crossed the Urals and thousands of miles of steppes till they reached the border of China. Then they turned around and headed back toward St. Petersburg, stopping for a time to study the life in the Caspian Sea.

Humboldt brought back new knowledge of the mountain ranges of Asia, of Siberia's climate and magnetic changes, of plant and animal life, and so on. But what impressed him most was the people of Central Asia. In a letter to a friend after his return he wrote: "The expedition to the Altai [mountains] on the confines of Chinese Mongolia and on the borders of the Caspian Sea—a journey of more than 13,500 miles, which I have just accomplished, has left on my mind some grand impressions. It is the people, especially the great nomad population, which has excited my interest far more than the majestic rivers or the snow-capped peaks. The imagination is led back to the primeval days when whole nations were in perpetual migration. The history of the past finds a striking exemplification in the fact that in our own day 1,300,000 Kirghizians are still leading a wandering life, transporting themselves on their wagons. We have been certified of this by history, but I have a mania for seeing everything with these old eyes of mine."

Two years before his Russian trip, Humboldt had moved from Paris to Berlin. He was now chamberlain to the king of Prussia. Some of his friends deplored his acceptance of an official position, especially under a monarchy that was neither constitutional nor enlightened. But the aging Humboldt liked court life and needed money. Besides, he had conceived the idea of doing a new book that would be a monument to his life of scientific study. It was to be called *Cosmos,* and it would be both a history of man's knowledge of the world and a survey of all that was known about the earth and the heavens. The book he finally produced in five volumes was a magnificent description of the physical world. It gave an exhaustive account of all the knowledge in natural science that had been accumulated up to the middle of the nineteenth century.

Humboldt worked tirelessly, advising King Frederick Wilhelm III, writing thousands of letters, and helping all who sought his aid—particularly young scientists. He assisted the naturalist Louis Agassiz in getting to America. He befriended Karl Friedrich Gauss, the mathematical genius of the century, and helped innumerable young scientists to secure posts in German universities.

When the king died, Humboldt continued as chamberlain to his successor, King Frederick Wilhelm IV. The duties of his position had become irksome. "I live," he said, "in the midst of the glitter of outward splendor and in the enjoyment of the romantic affection of a noble prince, yet in a moral and intellectual isolation necessarily enforced by the stunted intellects of this divided, erudite, and morose country—a true desert. . . ."

Long before Humboldt died in 1859, at the age of ninety, he had become a legend. In Berlin he was a monument sought out by visitors as Westminster Abbey was in London and the Coliseum in Rome. He knew something about everything and more than any living person about so many things. His prodigious memory made him a walking encyclopedia. Nevertheless it was his American travels that constituted his life's greatest work. The boldness of their conception, the dangers and hardships, and the enormous range of things he observed and investigated—these inspired men's enthusiasm and aroused their admiration. Although Humboldt lived a full and active life for fifty-five years after his return from America, his journeys as a young man on the Orinoco and in the Andes were the heart and core of his life.

Charles Darwin called Humboldt the "parent of a grand progeny of scientific travelers." A whole generation of naturalists was inspired to explore South America after him. Darwin was fired by Humboldt's writings to undertake his famous "Voyage of the Beagle," which led to the theory of evolution. In South America Darwin wrote that Humboldt, "like another sun," illumined everything he beheld. Alfred Russell Wallace, who came to a theory of evolution independently of Darwin, was also inspired by Humboldt to visit the tropics. So was Henry W. Bates, whose *Travels on the Amazon* became one of the great natural-history travel books of the English-speaking world.

Men have traveled for pleasure and for adventure. Some have traveled out of boredom; others to seek wealth, forgetfulness, or escape in a "tropical paradise." Humboldt traveled because he was fascinated by this earth, by its varied and changing surface, by what lay beneath it, and by the heavens above. For him, to live was to seek to know everything possible about this exciting "cosmos."

Humboldt's passport of 1798 expressed simply and completely his life's work: "Traveling for the acquisition of knowledge."

HUMBOLDT IN HIS STUDY

SOURCES AND SELECTIONS

The sources of the selections are abbreviated as follows:

PN   *Personal Narrative of Travels to the Equinoctial Regions of America During the Years 1799-1804,* by Alexander von Humboldt, translated by Thomasina Ross, 3 vols. London & New York, George Routledge and Sons, 1852.

VN   *Views of Nature,* by Alexander von Humboldt, translated by Otté and Bohn. London, Bohn, 1850.

KNS   *Political Essay on the Kingdom of New Spain,* by Alexander von Humboldt, translated by J. Black, 4 vols. London, Longman, Hurst, Rees, Orme, and Brown, 1811.

R   *Researches Concerning the Institutions and Monuments of the Ancient Inhabitants of America,* by Alexander von Humboldt, translated by Helen M. Williams, 2 vols. London, Longman, Hurst, Rees, Orme, and Brown, J. Murray and H. Colburn, 1814.

B   *Life of Alexander von Humboldt,* edited by Karl C. Bruhns, translated by J. C. Lassell, 2 vols. London, Longmans, Green and Company, 1873.

SELECTIONS